Please renew/return this item by the last date shown.

So that your telephone call is charged at local rate, please call the numbers as set out below:

	From Area codes 01923 or 0208:	From the rest of Herts:
Renewals:	01923 471373	01438 737373
Enquiries:	01923 471333	01438 737333
Minicom:	01923 471599	01438 737599

L32b

FIELD SPORTS LIBRARY

MOLES AND THEIR CONTROL

Other Books by Guy N. Smith

Ferreting and Trapping for Amateur Gamekeepers

Hill Shooting and Upland Gamekeeping

Gamekeeping and Shooting for Amateurs

Ratting and Rabbiting for Amateur Gamekeepers

Profitable Fishkeeping

Tobacco Culture – A D.I.Y. Guide

Sporting and Working Dogs

Animals of the Countryside

MOLES AND THEIR CONTROL

By

GUY N. SMITH

With drawings by Pamela Blaxland

Published by:
SAIGA PUBLISHING CO. LTD.
1 Royal Parade, Hindhead, Surrey
GU26 6TD   England

© GUY N. SMITH 1980

ISBN 0 904558 82 7

Typesetting by
Ebony Typesetting, Nr. Liskeard, Cornwall
Printed and bound by The Pitman Press, Bath.

Published by:
SAIGA PUBLISHING CO. LTD.
1 Royal Parade, Hindhead, Surrey
GU26 6TD   England.

DEDICATION

This book is dedicated to David Imrie, mole-catcher to the
Above Derwent Rabbit Clearance Society.

ACKNOWLEDGEMENTS

My thanks are offered to all those who assisted me in the writing and compilation of this book and, in particular, to:

Mr. J.W. Simpson, Regional Pest Officer, Ministry of Agriculture, Fisheries and Food, Wolverhampton for supplying information on trapping and poisoning.

Messrs. A. Fenn, F.H.T. Works, High Street, Astwood Bank, Redditch, Worcs. for supplying details of their new mole trap.

The Farmland Museum, Haddenham, Cambridge for allowing photographs to be taken of many of their fine mole traps.

David Parfitt, Bottisham, Cambridge for supplying many of the photographs used in this book.

Pamela Blaxland, Clun, Salop for undertaking the line-drawings.

CONTENTS

MONOCHROME ILLUSTRATIONS

AUTHOR'S INTRODUCTION

Mole-catching is probably the most under-rated of all 'field sports'. Indeed, few people regard it as a *sport* and look upon it more as a necessary task to be carried out by those responsible for the control of these small underground creatures. However, it is a duty which no amateur gamekeeper should overlook; moles are detrimental to his sport in a variety of ways which will be explained in greater detail later in this book. Not only will they kill a pheasant or partridge chick during a foray above ground, but they will also burrow beneath a coop during the nocturnal hours and frighten a sitting broody hen so that she will panic and trample her tiny charges to death. Furthermore, the tunnels dug by moles will provide an open entrance to otherwise secure game enclosures and these will be taken advantage of by weasels and other vermin. A better relationship can be established with the landlord from whom shooting is rented if it is obvious that the sporting tenant is making some effort to reduce the moles on his land.

Moles are mysterious and interesting creatures which will tax the skills of any trapper, whether amateur or professional. Their habits are difficult to observe because the greater part of their lives are spent below ground and, therefore, they also provide a challenge to the genuine naturalist.

The purpose of this book is twofold. It is intended primarily as a manual for the amateur mole-catcher, but also depicts a period of country life, of which the average person has little knowledge, through the lives of Frank Weale — a mole-catcher who operated in south Shropshire just after World War I — and David Imrie — another professional mole-catcher. We can only admire the courage of those who were prepared to 'do their own thing' in an era when most men were grateful for an agricultural labouring job during widespread unemployment and general recession.

Mole-catching should not be an irksome task, for the reader should derive satisfaction from the defeat of a wily foe. Man's instinct is to hunt, not simply for food as his ancestors did, but to destroy predators which rob him of that food supply even though it be growing crops in the fields. Far better for a harmful species to be controlled in this way than slaughtered by poison bait or gas.

Each and every one of us can play our part by taking on the role of the mole-catcher of yesteryear, learning by experience and becoming more proficient season after season. A text-book is simply not enough on its own. It can teach the novice the basics, the obvious pitfalls, and is always there for reference when the occasion arises. But the job itself must be learned the hard way, by trial and error, going out into the countryside and observing the ways of the creatures of the wild, recognising well-used 'runs' and learning not to waste time and effort by setting traps in places that are no longer used. It is an absorbing hobby, and as well as learning the art of catching moles regularly, it is hoped that the reader will become a proficient all-round naturalist.

Guy N. Smith

Black Hill,
Clun.

Pamela Blaxland

Frontispiece **The Common Mole** — a mysterious creature of the underworld.

1

Frank Weale — Professional Mole-Catcher

Figure 1.1   **The famous bridge at Ironbridge in the country of Frank Weale**

FRANK WEALE — PROFESSIONAL MOLE-CATCHER

EARLY DAYS

Little is known about the early life of the late Frank Weale. He was born around 1890 and during the early part of his life worked on farmland at Sparchford, near Ludlow, in Shropshire. He was a distant relative of the Weales of the Borderland and the Weales of Warwick. Charles Weale was an early pioneer of photography, the son of a country landowner who, although he had graduated to the highly honoured profession of chartered-accountant, decided to forego his practice at Much Wenlock, in Shropshire, in favour of the camera.

In the 1870s the Weale family had split up, going their separate ways, with Charles setting up his own photographic business in Kings Lynn. However, the roots of the family remained in the Ludlow area and it is here that we first hear of young Frank on his return from service in the trenches; being one of the lucky ones who escaped almost unscathed except for a bullet wound in his leg which caused him to walk with a limp for the rest of his life.

Call of the country

It is not known for certain whether young Frank had any game-keeping experience, although his father was a farm-labourer and the boy had accompanied him into the fields and had taken an interest in the ways of the countryside. Some years ago I spent considerable time in trying to trace the Weale family-tree and it was then that I came across the name of the old mole-catcher. Surviving members of the last generation in that part of the country had stories to tell of Frank Weale (in some instances the name is spelt Wheale); reminiscences based on fact, tales of a man in moleskin breeches who worked the pasturelands with his traps, a remote figure who was only to be seen at certain times of the year, leaving in his wake lines of dead moles suspended from the fences.

Yet it was enough to piece this fascinating jig-saw together, forming a picture of one who made a success of that which he liked doing best in life. In fact, his reputation was such that towards the end of his days (he died in 1937), he supposedly refused a lucrative offer from a wealthy landlord to clear the moles on a sizeable estate because he could not fit the extra work into his already over-loaded seasonal schedule! From all this emerges the character of Frank Weale himself; an expert at his trade and one who left a store of experience behind him which has been passed on by word of mouth until finally I decided to set it all down in this volume in the hope that it might be beneficial to others.

However, before we examine the man more closely, let us first look at his ancestry so that we may note the contrast between wealthy landlord and labourer of those times; the origins of a professional mole-catcher.

The Weales of the Borderlands

Weale is an old Salopian border name of Saxon origin meaning wealth. It is derived from the Celtic word *weala* and in all probability the Celts envied their neighbours in the lush valleys from Shrewsbury to Hereford, for in those days wealth depended largely upon the fertility of the land. Saxon remains are scattered throughout this part of Britain where these early races had fled before invaders.

Many variations sprang from the name Weale: Weal, Wheal, Wheala, Wiel, and even Wheeler. The earliest records of this particular family are to be found in *The Visitation of Shropshire* which starts a family tree of 'Weale of Cotes and Shrewsbury' with Willus Weale of Cotes in 1396. The coat-of-arms is

4

probably connected with a parliament held at Shrewsbury by Richard II in 1398 when the King's power was absolute. He had banished the Duke of Hereford (Henry Bolingbroke) for a term of ten years. It is feasible that Willus Weale had Royalist sympathies and had served Richard.

There was no coat-of-arms before the Norman Conquest, and these earlier ones were in the form of scrolls, beginning about 1240. Earlier warring armies carried emblems, which served as rallying points, but these did not belong to families. In the thirteenth century armorial designs were embroidered on the surcoat worn over armour, and from this sprang the name 'coat-of-arms'.

The Weales of Cotes and Shrewsbury had arms with the motto: '*Harl 1396 Gulis abend gabone*' — azure between six Crescents argent' which, translated, is a red base with a band of gold and blue between six silver crescents. The fact that the crescents were inverted denotes that Willus Weale of Cotes was a second son. Cotes was a tiny village tucked away in the Shropshire hills, now spelt Coates.

Willus Weale had a son Edmundos who produced seven sons. Of these, the fourth son, Roger (or Rogeros) moved to Warwick, still supporting the royal cause and hoping for a distinguished office at the court in London. However, he remained in Warwick, and his family and descendants became established there. By the sixteenth century there were several families by the name of Weale in Warwick, and George Weale was the first Mayor of Warwick in 1664.

The most distinguished of the Weales of Warwick was Fulke Weale who was sheriff in 1648, and is remembered as the founder of an exhibition in that name at the grammar school there. Added to the family crest, among other embellishments, is a helmet turned aside which denotes *Esquire*, and was given to men holding a lifetime rank such as sheriff.

Of these same seven sons of Edmundos Weale, the youngest, Robertus, made outstanding achievements in religious fields, gaining a motto *A Cruce Salus* and a boar's head erect, differing from the speared dolphin of Weale of Warwick.

From its main stem in the borderlands, the Weale family spread out and multiplied. During the sixteenth and seventeenth centuries records of arms and family pedigrees were made by heralds journeying through the country, and these 'visitations' have proved invaluable to many people seeking to trace their ancestry.

Prior to 1837 there are no records at Somerset House, and the main source of information is to be found in church records. Unfortunately, many inscriptions on tombstones have been totally erased by the elements. Records on old vellum were treated with gall in Victorian times, supposedly to blacken the ink, but in the majority of cases it has served to obliterate it after a few decades.

Figure 1.2 **The Weale Coat-of-Arms**

At Tewkesbury a prominent tomb in the Abbey, set in the floor of the nave, is inscribed to Thomas Weale, an apothecary who died in 1779, a "good and worthy man". It would appear that he was a nephew of that George Weale who was the first mayor of Warwick.

George had become a family christian name of the Warwick branch in later centuries. There is a tomb in the floor of the church at Rowington, six miles from Warwick, of the Reverend George Weale, late vicar of Rowington and native of Warwick, who died in 1812 at the age of sixty-one. Alongside is the tomb of his successor, another George Weale and also a later vicar of Rowington, who died in 1824 aged seventy-nine. This latter man wrote a book, now extremely rare, on the history of the Weales of Warwick.

Of the earlier Weales, the two sheriffs were probably buried in the church or churchyard of St Mary at Warwick, but this church was destroyed by fire in 1698. Inscriptions on the old graves outside are now indecipherable.

Thus we return to Shropshire, to the country of Frank Weale.

Strangely, the little church at Culmington bears no record of this family although the Weales were local landowners. There are many gaps in the family tree. The branches have grown and spread even across the Atlantic whence the Weales of New York came in search of their ancestors in Tewkesbury Abbey. The Weales were not famous, but they blended in with the history of our nation and played their part in the destiny of our rural life.

FRANK WEALE LEARNS TO CATCH MOLES

So we have Frank Weale, and the reader may well wonder why a man whose ancestry was nobility turned to the humble trade of mole-catching. As the twentieth century progressed, so the large estates began to split up. No longer could landowners afford the upkeep of vast acreages; previous tenants were given the opportunity to purchase the land which hitherto they had

7

rented. The whole structure of Britain was changing.

Frank Weale plied his trade towards the end of a golden era. Having become fascinated by the birds and beasts of the countryside, farm work for him was a drab routine. The gun, his father's old 14-bore muzzle-loader, kept principally for the purpose of scaring flocks of sparrows off the cornfields, held much more interest for him than the hoe in the turnip field. Yet his sporting potential was limited. Unlike today, when farm-labourers are often permitted to shoot rabbits and pigeons almost as a recognised 'perk', young Frank soon discovered that the gamekeepers were not prepared to tolerate such liberties. As a result he was banned from using the gun in the fields where he worked. It was a bitter blow and yet he was not to be deterred. He sought other means of taking game, but this, too, was short-lived when his father discovered that he had been snaring rabbits.

It appeared that every sporting door was closed to Frank Weale. He was not allowed to shoot, trap, or snare. The game was the property of the landowner, and the gamekeeper relied upon the rabbits to supplement his meagre income and, in addition, would not tolerate any amateur interfering with vermin control.

Then, one day whilst strolling across some pastureland, Frank Weale noticed the scores of molehills, unsightly mounds of fresh earth on the lush green grass. He remembered seeing some rusty mole-traps hanging up in the woodshed at home. Surely nobody would object to him catching a few moles! He had heard that the skins fetched a few pence apiece and were used in the manufacture of breeches, gloves and caps.

That same evening he devoted his time to cleaning up the old traps and greasing them with tallow so that they worked smoothly. His father was sceptical. There was surely no harm in catching a few moles, but there was certainly no profit by the time one had painstakingly skinned and stretched the pelts of the tiny animals. But if it gave the boy some pleasure then it had served its purpose. A few moles less was neither here nor there and, anyway, Frank would soon tire of his new pursuit.

Progress was steady
Success was not instant for Frank Weale. He had no instructor, no manual to which to refer, only a few old traps and some common-sense. It was a fortnight before he caught his first mole. He made the obvious beginner's mistake of burying his traps directly below the mounds instead of digging down and finding the intersecting runs between the molehills. Even then his catches were few and far between. He tried using gloves when handling his traps, and as a result, in the weeks which followed, his catches increased by 50%.

He was learning all the time, success spurring him on, encouraging him to experiment. Skinning, for instance, was not the simple task which he had imagined. His first few efforts were totally rejected by the furrier, even a slight tear rendering the skins useless. So he took to using the blade of a 'cut-throat' razor to enable him to cut more delicately. Well-stretched skins fetched higher prices than those which had not been tacked out to their full limit. Every extra penny counted!

Whether or not Frank Weale had any intention of becoming a professional mole-catcher in those early days we shall never know. Certainly he was supplementing his small agricultural wage and there was little competition, for the regular mole-catchers were few and far between with vast areas to cover.

FULL TIME OCCUPATION

By the time he was in his mid-twenties Frank Weale was catching moles for a living, and being paid 2/6d per acre by the landlords around Sparchford. As an added bonus he had moleskins for the furrier, now expertly flayed; winter pelts that were properly stretched and commanding the highest prices. Only towards the end of the season did he hang his catches on the fences bordering his trapping territory.

By the end of that first season his fame had spread and offers to trap moles were coming in from as far afield as Knighton and Bishop's Castle.

On his return from World War I Weale found that he could treble the agricultural wage, which he would then have been earning, by concentrating on mole-catching. Moleskins were much in demand and were fetching three shillings (15 pence) each whilst mole-traps could be purchased at three shillings a dozen.

The persistence of Frank Weale, the son of a farm labourer, had paid off. He had embarked upon a career which was destined to last for the rest of his life.

THE WEALES AND RURAL PHOTOGRAPHY

In view of the interest of the Weale family in photography, a brief outline of the subject in early days is thought to be appropriate.

It is approximately 150 years since photography was first recognised as a quick and efficient means of reproducing a picture. Certainly, the work of the early photographers was in no way comparable with that of the famous artists of the day, yet they also paid great attention to detail. Some early pioneers in this field became famous, whilst others, like the Weales, although not making the headlines, certainly made a contribution to the progress of this newly discovered dimension to art.

Generally, the country photographer took upon himself the trappings of the artist. His studio was often large with as much glass in the roof and sides as possible, for these were the days before arc-lights and the most had to be made of natural daylight; highlights were picked out on subjects by the use of white reflectors on stands. Among the photographers' props were stage settings of painted backdrops on rollers, reproduction furniture, palms in pots, draped curtains and statuettes.

Figure 1.3 **The country photographer**
Playing an essential part in recording the history of life in the country, here we see a Victorian photographer capturing a flooded landscape.

An essential part of daylight portraiture was re-touching, a task which demanded extreme care; I can well remember when my grandmother used to pore for hours over the lectern-like re-touching desk. Often in Victorian prints this was overdone, resulting in what is known as the 'chocolate-box effect'. Today this problem can be overcome by the adjustment of artificial lighting which despenses with re-touching altogether.

The Weale family dispersed for training and experience, eventually setting up their own studios in different towns. The younger members grew up in the atmosphere of a photographic world in the days when there were no light-meters, nor any of the accessories which turn amateurs into good photographers today. Their judgement of shutter speeds and apertures was learned by experience and eventually they became almost infallible in this respect. I still have several of their cameras which are unwieldy in comparison with their modern counter-

Figure 1.4 **Thornton-Pickard camera**

parts. Amongst them is a **Thornton-Pickard** with its squeeze-bulb and little blind-shutter, and also the massive '12 x 10' for outdoor photographs. There are also smooth fitting mahogany slides for the glass negatives.

The country photographer played a great part in the lives of all classes of clientele. Important and wealthy families called upon him regularly to record various events of their lives and the growth of their children. He was an historian of local affairs, of buildings and the country scene. It was a pleasant position from which to enjoy the once leisurely world and enabled them to believe in the artistic qualities of this new art until science, technology and commercialism joined the flood of an expansion which was to put the camera into every man's hand.

Figure 1.5 **The country scene.**

14

2

The Natural History
of the Mole

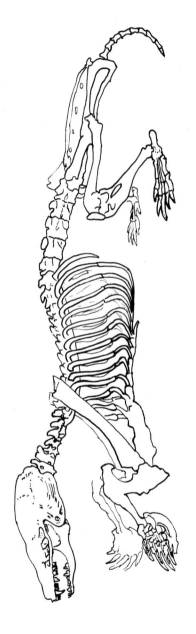

Figure 2.1 **Skeleton of a mole** — showing the fine bone structure.

THE NATURAL HISTORY
OF THE MOLE

Moles are members of the family *Talpidae* and several different species may be found around the world. They are similar in many respects to shrewmice and are so closely linked that we cannot study one without learning something about the other. For this reason a detailed look at the main species in each group is necessary, as well as a brief comparison with some of the other animals of the countryside.

OTHER ANIMALS OF THE COUNTRYSIDE

A summary of the different mammals found in Britain and some of the moles found abroad is given below.

Winged Animals
Bats
Insect-Eating Animals
Hedgehog
Shrew
   Common
   Islay
   Pigmy
   Water
Mole
   Common
   Hairy-Tailed (U.S.A.)
   Star-Nosed (U.S.A.)
   Web-Footed (U.S.A.)
   Japanese (Japan)
   Desmans (U.S.S.R.)
   Mole-shrews (Japan, North America)

Rodents
Hare
  Brown
  Mountain
Rabbit
Squirrel
  Red
  Grey
Mouse
  Harvest
  House
  Long-tailed Field
  Dormouse
Rat
  Black
  Brown

Flesh-eating Animals
Fox
Weasel Tribe
  Stoat
  Weasel
  Polecat
  Pine Marten
  Otter
  Badger
Wild Cat

Those of the above-mentioned creatures which are also burrowing animals:

Shrews
Moles
Rabbits
Mice
Rats
Foxes
Badgers

Others which live in burrows, usually making use of those dug by other creatures:

Stoat
Weasel
Polecat
Pine Marten

18

Figure 2.2 **Weasel** — this creature often hunts moles below ground and is sometimes caught in a mole-trap.

The pine marten will sometimes use an old crow's nest or a squirrel's drey whilst the former three animals will, in most cases, take over rabbit burrows.

Of all the above animals, the mole is unique in that it lives entirely below ground with the exception of the occasional foray above the surface to search for young birds or other carrion. It is almost impossible to categorise all the different species correctly into either carnivores, insectivores or herbivores. For example, although the mole's diet consists almost entirely of worms and insects, it will also eat flesh, whilst the badger, besides eating insects and flesh, will also eat vegetation.

As has been said, there are a number of different species of moles to be seen throughout the world, including mole-shrews and desmans. It is as well, therefore, that we acquaint ourselves with these other members of the family of moles and other related creatures so that we can fully understand our own mole, the **European** or **common mole** (*Talpa europea*).

Figure 2.3 **The mysterious mole** — spending most of its life underground, this creature is rarely seen by man.

The Mole Family

Although similar in many ways to shrewmice, moles and desmans are sufficiently different to justify belonging to a family of their own. *Talpidae* skulls have an arch connecting the jaw with the upper ear. On the rear of the skull of shrewmice the internal ear is little more than an open ring but in moles and desmans the ear is more pronounced.

Most members of the Talpidae family are burrowers and a few are good swimmers. All have long skulls and small eyes and ears. The front limbs are placed well-forward on the body to assist digging.

The mole species are not so numerous as those of the shrewmice and are mostly distributed over Europe, North America and Asia.

Mole-Shrews

Moles are closely linked with shrews. There are only two species of mole-shrews (*Urotrichus*), which are to be found in Japan and North America. These creatures are much smaller than moles and do not have webbed feet. The *szechuen* is grey in colour with teeth similar to the shrew but has all the outward features of a mole.

Hairy-Tailed Mole (Scapanus americanus)

Several species of hairy-tailed moles are to be found in the U.S.A. Whilst similar to the star-nosed mole this creature prefers drier terrain.

Star-Nosed Mole (Condylura cristata)

This creature, a native of North America, takes its name from the shape of its nose. The body is about 5 inches in length with the tail being approximately $4\frac{1}{2}$ inches long. Large mounds of earth mark the course of its underground tunnels on arable land but on grassland it travels at a much greater depth. In appearance it resembles the European mole with the exception of its nose. The strange circle of tentacles around the nose act in the same way that whiskers aid a cat in scenting its prey, the mole being able to detect the presence of earthworms by this means. These tentacles are barely noticeable in young moles, growing as the animal attains maturity.

Web-Footed Mole (genus Scalops)

Another North American species, this mole has thick fur to which the soil in its burrows does not stick. It lives almost entirely on grubs, worms and other insects which are found below ground. It is considered a threat to growing crops as it is particularly fond of arable land, having a liking for well-irrigated soil which it can excavate rapidly.

Desmans (genus Myogale)

These unusual looking creatures are a link between shrew-mice and voles. They have completely webbed feet and a long nose; the long tail is scaly. The desman found in the Soviet Union is

Figure 2.4 **Star-Nosed Mole**
A native of North America and similar to the European Mole with the exception of its extraordinary nose.

the largest of the species having an overall length of 16 inches, including the tail. The thick fur has a soft undercoat, is dark brown in colour but is slate-grey underneath. Mostly it is to be found in south-eastern Russia although fossilised remains have been found on the Norfolk coast.

Shrews
Common Shrew (Sorex araneus)
The common shrew is a harmless little creature whose diet consists solely of insects. It is a mere 3 inches in length, including the tail, and has a long pointed snout with an abundance of whiskers. In colour it is almost black, having a close, silky fur that is lighter on the underparts.

This shrew does not hibernate although it spends most of the winter amidst piles of dead leaves and in sheltered hedgerows. It is capable of climbing a tree but can only burrow in light soil and, in most cases, it uses the established burrows of mice. It is also able to swim.

The common shrew breeds throughout the summer into early autumn and has several litters, with usually from four to eight young in each.

Like mice and voles its enemies are cats, hawks and owls, corvines and, of course, both grass snakes and adders.

The common shrew is found throughout Britain but not in Ireland. It is also to be encountered at high altitudes, another factor which it has in common with the mole.

The Islay Shrew (Sorex granti)
This is to be found only on the Isle of Islay and is listed by naturalists as a distinct species.

Pigmy Shrew (Sorex minutus)
Not only is the pigmy shrew the smallest of the shrew family, it is also the smallest animal in the British Isles. It is also to be found in Ireland.

It is an inch shorter in length than the common shrew and is

Figure 2.5 **Shrews** — close relatives of the Common Mole.

24

brown and white in colour, the snout and tail being proportionally thicker than that of its larger relative.

It uses the existing burrows of mice but has often been known to nest in the open. The female gives birth to two litters during the summer months with from two to eight young in each, the nest being woven into a hollow ball in much the same way as that of the harvest mouse except that it is constructed on the ground.

Water Shrew (Neomys fodiens)
The water shrew is the largest of the shrew family with a body length of up to 4 inches, including the tail. The upper fur is dark, in some instances almost black, but lighter fur is underneath. The snout is short and thick and the ears are hidden beneath the fur. Its adaptation to a watery habitat can be seen by its thick tail which is used effectively as a rudder and by its fur which is thicker and more waterproof than that of any of the other shrews.

It frequents the banks of streams where it makes its burrow. It does not hibernate and sometimes in winter it can be seen swimming beneath the ice. The female breeds twice during the summer months with as many as eight in each litter.

Probably of all the shrews this one is nearest to the mole in appearance. It is often found at elevations of over 1,000 feet swimming in mountain streams. It is widespread throughout Britain but is not found in Ireland, nor in some of the Scottish islands.

Hedgehog *(Erinaceus europaeus)*
The hedgehog does not, as his name suggests, spend all his time living in hedgerows. He likes cover, thick herbacious borders, piles of dead undergrowth and anything, in fact, which affords him privacy and protection. A nocturnal animal, his only real enemies, apart from Man and dogs, are the fox and the badger.

The male is approximately 9 inches long, the female an inch or so shorter. The sharp spines are really stiff hairs which protect

Figure 2.6 **Hedgehogs.**

26

the whole squat body, with the exception of the underside, the head being drawn back into these when danger threatens. This animal is also able to eject an obnoxious odour in the manner of the polecat.

Although hedgehogs were once eaten readily by gypsies they are now seldom regarded as edible. Probably the highest mortality rate occurs on the roads; seldom will a motorist travel many miles without encountering one in the headlights of his vehicle. Contrary to popular belief, Mr. Prickles is *not* a slow mover. He can run quite fast yet when crossing a road it would seem that he has suicidal tendencies. We can only conclude that on being dazzled by oncoming lights he at once stops and rolls himself into a ball.

The hedgehog is both beneficial and detrimental to the countryside. In the garden he is useful, eating slugs, mice, and an occasional snake when he comes across one. Indeed, most gardeners welcome his presence while, in constrast, the game-keeper regards him as vermin. This is due to his fondness of eggs and the fact that he will also devour the fledglings of most birds. Once he knows his way about the game preserves he will continue to raid the rearing field until he falls prey to one of the keeper's tunnel traps.

The hedgehog shows little cunning and is easily caught. He makes an admirable pet in a garden but should not be confined to an enclosure or cage of any kind. It is far better to put a saucer of bread and milk ouside for him after darkness and he will then remain in the vicinity indefinitely.

He is one of the few animals which hibernates throughout the entire winter, rolling himself up into a ball amidst a pile of dead leaves at the bottom of a thick hedgerow or in the corner of a walled garden. He will hibernate anywhere, in fact, where he has shelter from the strong winds which might otherwise blow away his winter quarters. His body temperature drops and he is kept alive by a layer of fat which he has built up during the autumn. To disturb him is to kill him, for once he is awoken he will not be able to return to that state which enables him to survive the rigours of winter.

THE COMMON MOLE *(Talpa europea)*

This is the variety of mole which will be of most interest to the reader; the mysterious underground creature against which the amateur gamekeeper must pit his wits. The mole is still not fully understood by Man as most of its life is spent below ground, but it is an aggressive creature which has been known to attack and kill animals larger than itself. It is very much a 'loner' and resents the presence of other moles in its own territory. It has fascinated people for centuries, and even before the advent of modern steel traps the hunter attempted to catch it in a variety of ways. It was known as *Uir each*, an old Gaelic name meaning 'burrower in the soil'.

Habits

The common mole is cylindrical in shape, the forelegs set well-forward and the skull pointed; a factor which is of considerable assistance in tunnelling. The fur is dark grey, not black as is often supposed, and is almost like velvet in texture. Indeed, the mole is often referred to as *'the gentleman in velvet'*.

Different 'off-colours' are also found, such as white, white and black and, recently, in Oxfordshire an apricot-coloured mole was found. These colours arise from the accidental mating of two moles whose recessive colour genes carry an apricot or other colour factor.

The feet serve as pickaxes and shovels during the mole's digging operations, the front feet breaking up the soil whilst the rear ones push it behind. The head is also used to assist this tunelling. It has forty-four teeth and males weigh 4 oz, females 3 oz or less.

Small eyes are hidden in the fur, a factor which causes many to believe that the animal is blind. However, although the mole is not completely blind its eyesight is decidedly poor, something

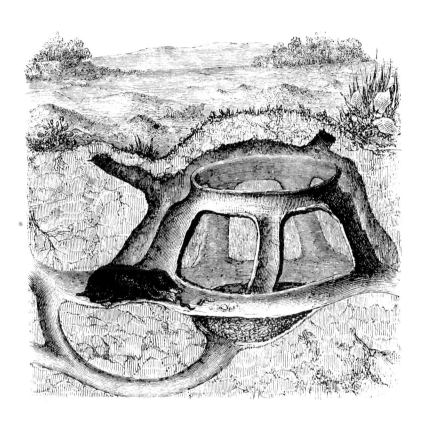

Figure 2.7 **Interior of a molehill**
(From an old print)

which is only to be expected in a creature which spends almost all its life in subterranean darkness.

There are no external ears yet its hearing is acute, the soil assisting the mole in picking up even the slightest vibration. The muzzle is sensitive in spite of its constant boring through the soil, and the tail is also used as an auxiliary 'early-warning system'. Very seldom is the mole surprised by an attack from the rear.

The overall length of the mole is about 6 inches, and beneath the fur is a very thick skin which only the sharpest knife is capable of cutting through. It is indeed a compact creature combining all the necessary qualities for an underground life.

Breeding

Moles usually breed in their second year. They mate from March to May and three or four young are born, usually in June. Baby moles are about 2 inches long at birth, and grow hair after a fortnight. This is a cream colour at first, turning to off-white, and only darkens when they reach maturity. They are not capable of fending for themselves until they are five weeks old. The period of gestation is four weeks.

The nursery is generally to be found in the soil beneath hedgerows and other secluded places where there is less likelihood of danger from either humans or predators; thick hawthorn acting as a safety barrier. On clay soil, however, the nest is usually to be found at ground level. Obviously the aim will be to keep the nest dry and warm.

Moles prepare the nursery by lining it with dry grass which they collect by poking their snouts out of the holes and dragging the bedding inside. In this respect they are similar to badgers.

The female will protect her young savagely, even to the extent of biting the fingers of an interfering human hand! Young moles mature at around sixteen weeks and are often seen travelling above ground during the summer months. An old belief is that the young are driven from the tunnels by the males, but more likely the reason is that they are not yet able to burrow for food themselves so they forage for it on the surface. Moles have a life span of around four years.

Food

The mole eats its own weight daily, relying in winter mostly on earthworms; in summer it consumes about 50% earthworms to 50% of slugs, beetles, centipedes, leather-jackets, spiders, frogs and lizards. It will eat carrion, usually a dead bird or mouse, which it comes across on an expedition above ground, but never touches vegetable matter. The mole builds up a store of worms simply by biting through their heads so that they are unable to escape by burrowing. In this way they are kept alive for long periods and devoured during times when food is scarce.

One of the reasons why it is difficult to keep moles in captivity is because of the quantity of worms needed daily. After a period of flooding moles will generally desert an area for some considerable time. This is because the insect life in the soil has been destroyed and only when it has re-established itself will the mole return to its former haunts.

Hibernation

The true hibernators amongst our native wildlife are bats, snakes, lizards, frogs and toads. Other animals such as squirrels merely sleep during cold weather, emerging to hunt for food during milder spells.

The mole does not hibernate. It was always believed to do so because far less activity was observed on pastureland during the winter months, but this is due to the fact that it has burrowed deeper in its constant hunt for earthworms which have gone well below the surface in an attempt to escape frosts.

Activity

Moles usually work for five hours and rest for three, being most active just after daybreak and in the evenings. Frank Weale claimed that moles fed at four, eight and twelve o'clock but we must only take this as an average. Like most animals, moles hunt when they are hungry and sleep when they are tired.

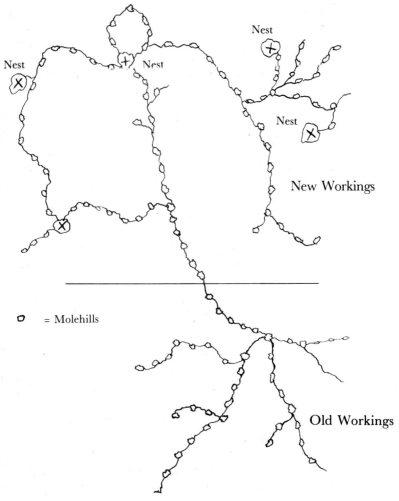

Nest

Nest

Nest

Nest

New Workings

◖ = Molehills

Old Workings

Figure 2.8 **The mole's fortress**
Showing an extension of the old workings made for breeding purposes.

They are capable of travelling at 3 m.p.h., and can burrow out of sight in thirty seconds. They are also able to swim and often prefer to cross a river in this way than to tunnel beneath it. They do not like swampy ground, preferring well-tilled soil. Unfortunately, this often takes them to well-kept gardens or down beneath a newly-sown tennis court! An adult male can dig a tunnel 100 yards long in the course of a day.

*The Mole' Fortress** (see Figure 2.8)
The mole's fortress is usually constructed beneath a hill, the spreading roots of a tree, or any place which offers protection. This fortress is recognisable by a dome of solid compressed earth, at the base of which is a circular gallery communicating with a smaller upper gallery by means of several passages. Inside the lower, and under the upper, of these galleries is the dormitory, from which there is access to the upper gallery through another three passages. From this place is the tunnel by which the mole reaches the opposite side of the fortress; there are various galleries joining this tunnel which the mole is continually extending in its search for food.

A fortress is made by a process of gradual construction rather than an all-out effort by the inhabitants. It is their hunting ground, their travels taking them wherever there is an abundance of worms. **Although fortresses bear a similarity, no two are alike.**

From the big chamber the first tunnel goes downwards, then rises again into the main thoroughfare. Some half-dozen passages open out from the external circular gallery, each returning in a roughly semi-circular route, joining the main passage at various intervals.

The main passage links the habitation area, the different parts of the fortress and the tunnels leading to the hunting area. It is

---

* Some modern naturalists have expressed doubts on the true nature of the so-called "fortress". Below the mound is the nest, but the upper part simply consists of the surplus earth and escape tunnels.

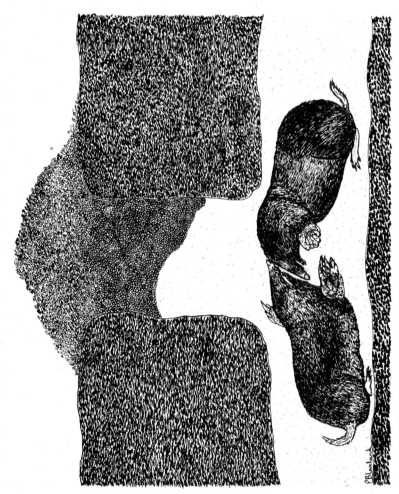

Figure 2.9 **The fight** — a meeting below ground often results in a fierce fight between two males.

just wide enough for a mole to travel along it but impossible for two to pass; sometimes a meeting results in a fierce fight to the death! The walls are smooth due to the constant mole traffic. Occasionally, several moles use a *main* route without undue aggression towards one another, but few are foolish enough to trespass on another's hunting ground.

The mole-catcher is extremely fortunate if he locates the main artery of a fortress for here his traps should catch daily, as opposed to taking one mole from each hunting area.

Moles burrow to a greater or lesser depth according to the soil conditions and obstacles which impede their course. In open land where the earth is well-tilled, seldom will a mole travel deeper than 4 or 5 inches, but when it meets roads or streams it will be necessary for it to go down as deep as 18 inches or 2 feet. Seldom do the tunnels collapse. If there is a convenient drainpipe the mole will use it.

The alleys leading from the main passage often contain a plentiful supply of food and the mole then constructs subsidiary alleys in quest of this abundance of worms. The quality and moisture content of the soil regulates the worm population and exceptional weather conditions will determine the presence or absence of the moles. For instance, during the long drought of 1976 few molehills were observed. The creatures had burrowed to a greater depth following their prey which had been forced down by the parched top soil.

As well as excavations in search of worms, moles sometimes follow the course of their prey *along the surface* where gentle rain, particularly in the spring, has brought the worms to the top. This method is used particularly by female moles carrying young as it is considerably easier than tunnelling.

The mole is a thirsty creature and often frequents ponds and streams. Sometimes it even sinks its own 'wells', holes a couple of inches deep which fill with water in damp ground.

It is interesting to note that there are no moles in Ireland.

Moults
The mole undergoes three moults each year. The first is in the spring, the second between July and September, and the third in late autumn or early winter.

The Enemies of the Mole
The Mole has a variety of enemies:

Tawny Owls will swoop down on an unsuspecting mole during one of the creatures forays above ground.

Weasels will often traverse mole tunnels, and are the only creatures which are small enough and fierce enough to take on the mole in its own domain.

Stoats are too large to hunt below ground like their smaller cousin, the weasel, but they will not ignore the opportunity of killing a mole on the surface.

Figure 2.10   **Tawny Owl** — the silent nocturnal enemy of the mole when above ground.

36

Cats and dogs will always kill a mole if the opportunity arises but they will not eat it. Usually a dog will roll on a mole which it has slain.

The fox has a similar outlook towards moles. Reynard will wait by a molehill until he sees the earth moving, then he will pounce, tossing the mole out into the open and rolling on it.

Mole flea *(Hystrichopsylla talpae talpae)*: this mite is the smallest of the mole's enemies.

Legends and Myths
Moles were held in high esteem by the Jacobites after the accidental death of William III in 1702 when his horse stumbled on a molehill in Hampton Court Park. This molehill is shown in the King's statue in St. James's Square, London. As a result of this mishap the favourite Jacobite toast was to '*The Little Gentleman in Black Velvet*'.

Over the centuries country folk have always believed that when moles were seen in woodlands a period of drought was imminent. More likely the creatures were making surface hunts in search of carrion.

The mole-catcher of old, before the days of Frank Weale, often had a market for the dried front feet of his catches. There is an old superstition that the carrying of them will ward off rheumatism. This custom is still carried on today in parts of East Anglia.

It was also a common belief that all moles were males until the spring when half of them became females. Probably this superstition was derived from the fact that the majority of moles trapped during the winter months were males busily hunting, the females being more active in the spring prior to preparing their breeding quarters. Ignorance, too, may have played its part for, except during the breeding season, the genital organs of the mole are very much alike in both sexes.

Sounds

The mole is not the silent underground creature which we might imagine it to be. When feeding it 'twitters' and squeals loudly when frightened or fighting.

FOR AND AGAINST THE MOLE

The mole is not simply a villain of the countryside to be destroyed at all costs. Indeed, in some cases this creature is beneficial to agriculture and, therefore, the object of mole-catching is to **control** the numbers and not to attempt extermination. We must not forget conservation — no bird or animal should be persecuted to the point of extinction. Let us then, in all fairness to the mole, weigh the 'pro's' and 'con's' and determine just to what extent we should trap, and in which places the mole does the most harm. Hedgehogs, for example, are detrimental to the game preserves yet beneficial to the garden. Therefore, they must be controlled in the former and encouraged in the latter. So it is with the mole.

Damage done by the mole.

There will always be moles in the vicinity of any game preserve, and where broody hens are used to incubate eggs or rear day-old chicks these burrowers will constitute a danger. Broody hens will become frightened when they hear moles working beneath the coop and may panic and smash eggs or trample chicks.

Even more dangerous is the fact that weasels hunting moles along their tunnels will find they have an easy access to the otherwise secure pheasant pens. During one night these bloodthirsty little creatures will slaughter every poult or chick in the pen. Coops can be safeguarded against this by the installation of wooden floors but this is costly and also means additional cleaning out. **It is far easier to get rid of the moles!**

Moles will also take a small pheasant or partridge chick on the occasions when they hunt above ground. In fact, little can be said in favour of moles on the rearing-field except that during dry weather the molehills will be favoured by pheasants for dust-bathing. In addition to this there will also be a wealth of insects for them to feed upon which will have been brought to the surface as the mole throws up the soil.

Moles are not looked upon favourably by either farmers or gardeners. As has been stated before, these animals favour well-tilled soil and for this reason a garden or field of growing crops is particularly attractive to them. During the spring, seed-drills will be disturbed and in the summer they will uproot growing plants. Mice will often follow along a seed-bed where a mole has been active and devour the exposed seeds. Ironically, in winter, when the mole's activities would be least harmful, it burrows deeply, away from the surface where it causes the damage, after

Figure 2.11 **Damage done by the mole** — their workings below ground will often frighten broody hens and cause them to trample thier eggs or chicks.

Figure.2.12 The gentleman in black velvet (Courtesy: Pat Lakin).

40

worms which are seeking to escape the frosts!

Valuable pastureland is ruined in the spring; whole fields turned into an unsightly mass of fresh soil heaps. Not only will fields of hay be spoiled, but the stones brought to the surface by the moles can seriously damage farm machinery. They are also responsible for fouling silage which, in turn, leads to harmful fermentation and their molehills also act as seed-beds for vigorous colonising weeds.

Not only the farmer and the gardener suffers loss by the activities of the mole; bowling greens, tennis-courts and football pitches can be ruined overnight on the eve of an important competition.

The mole is not simply confined to rural areas — he is apt to turn up anywhere and not even the walled town garden is spared his depredations. There is no way of keeping out the 'little gentleman in velvet'. His numbers must be reduced to a minimum so that his activities are on a much smaller scale.

Benefits

Sometimes mole workings in the soil can prove beneficial. For example, land which is sorely in need of drainage can be rendered workable, as water which would otherwise lie on the surface seeps away via the maze of tunnels. However, in this age of mechanisation drainage rarely offers a serious problem, and farmers generally prefer to rely on their own efforts rather than those of the mole who would only become a nuisance once the land was fit for cultivation.

Yet nobody can dispute the good which the mole achieves in controlling harmful insects, such as leather-jackets, in the soil. This is possibly the animal's one redeeming factor, but we must accept that the harm which it does outweighs the good and therefore strict control is vital in the interests of everybody remotely connected with the land.

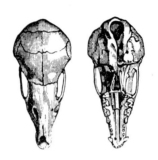

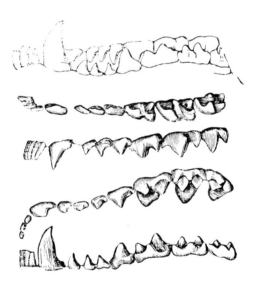

Figure 2.13 **Skull and teeth of a mole.**

3

Mole-Catching in
Olden Times

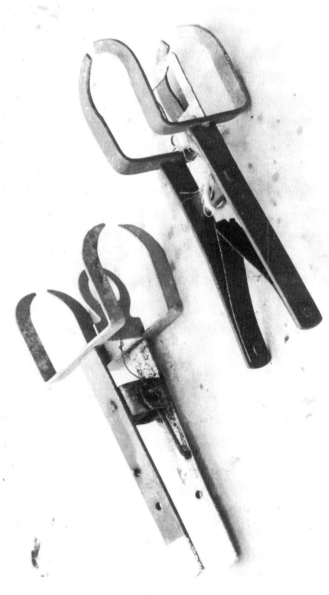

Figure 3.1 **Progress** — two examples of a Scissor-type Trap.
Top: Approximately five years old
Bottom: Approximately twenty-five to thirty years old.
(*Courtesy:* Farmland Museum, *photo courtesy:* D. Parfitt)

MOLE-CATCHING IN OLDEN TIMES

MOLE CONTROL

The attitude adopted towards moles and their control depends upon whether they should be tolerated for the benefits they bring or whether they should be exterminated altogether. Remember, they do eliminate many insect pests and, therefore, keeping down numbers and restricting them to particular areas where they can do little damage may be the best approach and compromise for some people.

Control may be viewed in two ways:

1. Moving the moles away from areas where they do damage; e.g. lawns and seed beds, to other parts where they do little or no damage and assist with drainage or clear insects.

2. Trapping and killing them so they are removed permanently.

Mole Squibs represent an attempt to move them from one area to another and many similar methods have been used in the past. Even going over the ground with a lawn mower powered by a noisy engine appears to have the desired effect of moving them on. However, most of the unorthodox methods concentrate on placing bottles, jars or other "disturbances" in the tunnels to frighten the mole by noises, fumes or unusual objects.

An extract from an eighteenth century *Sportsman's Dictionary* shows the general approach adopted to mole control in those days.

> "**MOLES** in the fields may be destroyed by taking a head or two of garlick, onion or leek, and put into their holes, and they will

45

run out as if frightened, and you may with a spear or dog take them.

"Or, pounded hellebore, white or black, with wheat flour, the white of an egg, milk and sweet wine or metheglin, make it into a paste, and put pellets as big as a small nut into their holes, they eat it with pleasure, and it will kill them.

"In places you would not dig nor break much, the fuming their holes with brimstone, garlic, or other unsavoury things, drives them away; and if you put a dead mole into a common haunt it will make them absolutely forsake it.

"Or, take a mole spear or staff, and where you see them cast, go lightly; but not on the side betwixt them and the wind, lest they percieve you; and at the first or second puting up of the earth, strike them with your mole staff downright, and mark which way the earth falls most: if the casts towards the left hand, strike somewhat on the right hand, and so on the contrary to the casting up of the plain ground, strike down, and there let it remain: then take out the tongue in the staff, and with the spattle or flat edge dig round about your grain to the end thereof, to see if you have killed her; and if you have missed her, leave open the hole, and step little, and perhaps she will come to stop the hole again, for they love but very little air, and then strike again; but if you miss her, pour into her hole two gallons of water, and that will make her come out for fear of drowning; mind them going out of a morning to feed, or coming home when fed, and you may take a great many."

A SCHOOL FOR MOLE-CATCHING

Before we study the methods used by Frank Weale to kill moles it is necessary for us to take a look at his predecessors and the way they operated against their tireless underground enemy.

One of the most diligent historians of the mole was **Henri le Court** *who established a school for mole-catching!* The professional mole-catcher is summed up, perhaps unfairly, in the following extract taken from Cassell's *Popular Natural History*, c. 1890:

"Like the ratcatcher, he belongs to a dubious class of persons who prefer a hazy-lazy life to the varied and honourable toils of the farm-labourer. And yet, the old proverb suggesting the pains to which idle people put themselves, has some illustration in his career. As his occupation is confined to those seasons when it does not materially interfere with crops, his traps cannot be set for several months together, and the frost of winter often prevents the pursuit of his calling, or interferes with its success. If then, by any means, he can eke out a subsistence, he may cherish his indolence as he lists. But let him obtain a job, and then truly it is no joke; for exclusive of the labour and delay in setting his traps, he frequently walks more than 20 miles a day; and this for the most part neither along good roads nor well-beaten paths, but over hedge and ditch, from farm to farm, and from field to field, on the lands of the owner or the occupier who contracts with him to destroy the moles.

"It is singular that this work should not be undertaken by persons living in the neighbourhood of the places where their services are sought. Yet, over a considerable extent of Scotland, as well as of Wales, the moles are destroyed by catchers who belong to some of the northern counties of England. They visit their employers at regular periods of the year, when their appearance is anticipated by the Scottish and Welsh farmers as certainly as the coming of the Irish haymakers and reapers is in the meadows and cornfields of England. The war they carry on with the moles almost amounts to one of extermination. The numbers that have been annually slaughtered are enormous. Mr Bell, the eminent naturalist, states that Mr Jackson, a very intelligent mole-catcher, who had followed the craft for thirty-five years, had destroyed from forty to fifty thousand."

Slaughter was wholesale even before the advent of modern traps. It would seem that Henri le Court's characterisation of the old mole-catcher was somewhat harsh, for such results could not have been achieved without hard labour. Neither was this role restricted to labouring classes with a lazy temperament for **Harcatius** was the mole-catching King of Parthia and Aristotle also wrote at great length about the art, and was obviously interested in the sport.

OLD MOLE-TRAPS

Four main types of traps were employed by the catchers of old:
  1. The falling block.

Figure 3.2 **Half-Barrel mole-trap**
The trap is set by using string and a Birch twig.
(*Courtesy:* Farmland Museum, *photo courtesy:* D. Parfitt)

48

2. The Wooden Barrel Trap.
   A half-barrel with horse-hair loops at either end and a wooden peg for the trigger which operated the spring mechanism which drew up the loops and held the mole. This was the forerunner of the later **Duffus Trap.**
3. A pot sunk in the mole's run; a pitfall trap with a wooden roof, baited with worms in the bottom.
4. The Nipper Trap.

The Wooden Barrel Trap
The Wooden Barrel Trap was probably the most favoured tool of the old mole-catcher. Its use undoubtedly goes back to the advent of organised husbandry, or at least to an era when grass became a valuable crop, when moles could no longer be allowed to destroy pasture and the potential of hay and silage.

The trap is relatively bulky with its bow spring. The string loops at each end need renewal at the start of every season to

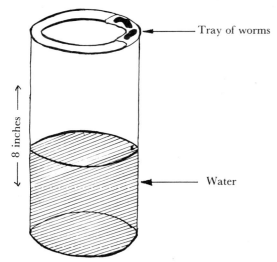

Tray of worms

8 inches

Water

Figure 3.3 **Sunken Pot or Pitfall Trap**
The top of the trap should be level with the top of the mole run. The mole will then fall into the water and drown.

49

Horsehair snares

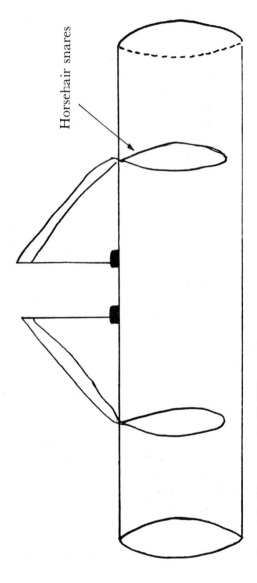

Figure 3.4 **Diagram of a Half-Barrel Trap**
This trap has horsehair snares at either end which will catch a mole coming from either direction. On occasions this trap has been known to catch two moles at one setting; the second mole scenting the first and being caught on investigating.

50

eliminate delay when time is valuable, as the 'trigger' which plugs the hole in the hump of the barrel can be lost if its tether rots.

The actual setting of the trap is time-wasting which means that an unnecessary amount of human scent is spread over it. The mole has a keen nose and this must always be borne in mind by the trapper, otherwise the trap may be 'soiled-up'. Indeed, a contemptuous mole will even throw soil over the normally conspicuous bow spring.

However, the Barrel Trap has continued to be used by professional mole destroyers because of its simple construction, its comparative effectiveness, and its durability.

The Nipper Trap

The inventor of the all-metal Nipper or Scissor Trap is apparently unknown or uncommonly modest. As the name implies, this trap nips its victim between prongs, which are operated by a V-spring, when the mole pushes away the metal trigger with its snout. It is also known as the Scissor Trap because of this action. However, the old professional mole-catchers seldom favoured this trap probably because small lumps of moist earth must be available in order to set it properly in position. If the Nipper Trap is placed loosely in a run the wily mole will suspect danger and act accordingly. However, for gardeners and householders who are not faced with the mammoth task of clearing moles from hundreds of acres of mixed farmland the Nipper has proved itself to be a useful trap.

Apart from the traps listed above, certain other types were also used. One of these, the **Patent Impassable Mole Trap**, was in use in the 1890s and is illustrated in Figure 3.6. It also became known as the **Guillotine Trap.**

Many home-made traps were developed by the old mole-catchers, (see Figure 3.7), using odd bits of wood and wire to construct efficient devices for killing and trapping their quarry.

Apart from traps and trapping, the mole-catcher also used a **snare** to catch moles. These snares were cleverly formed from

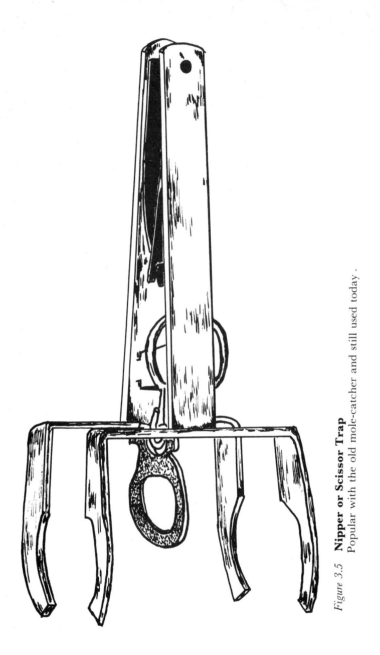

Figure 3.5 **Nipper or Scissor Trap**
Popular with the old mole-catcher and still used today.

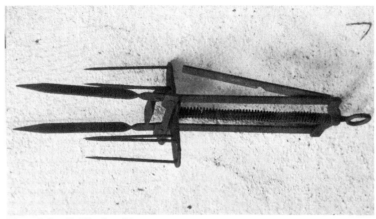

Figure 3.6 **Guillotine Trap**
Also known as the Patent Impassable Mole-Trap and used in the 1890s.
(*Courtesy:* Farmland Museum, *photo courtesy:* D. Parfitt)

Figure 3.7 **Home-made mole-trap**
This trap was made approximately forty years ago using odd pieces of wood and wire and was set using a length of spring steel.
(*Courtesy:* Farmland Museum, *photo courtesy:* D. Parfitt)

53

supple, young twigs and strong wire or twine. However, the setting of the snare was by far the longer method when compared with the multitude of traps available and its use gradually died out.

Figure 3.9 shows the basic type of trap that came into use in the 1900s. Made of cast iron complete with a moulded handle and shaped clay, this trap was the forerunner of the now common **Nipper** or **Scissor Trap.**

OTHER METHODS

Baiting
One ploy used by the old mole-catchers was to gather red worms from a manure heap, cork them up in a bottle, and store them in a hot-bed for a week or so. During this time the captive worms turned to a liquid which was used for baiting the mole traps by soaking a wad of cotton wool in the solution and placing it on the traps.

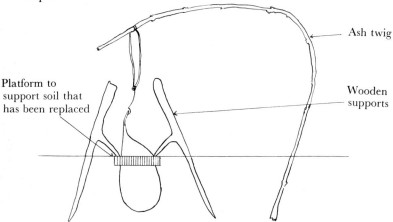

Ash twig

Platform to support soil that has been replaced

Wooden supports

Figure 3.8 **Snaring moles** — a method once employed by the old time mole-catcher.

Figure 3.9 **Early trap**
This trap, made in the early 1900s, was made from cast iron with a moulded handle and shaped clay.
(*Courtesy:* Farmland Museum, *photo courtesy:* D. Parfitt)

Dogs

Sometimes dogs were trained to hunt moles by working silently down-wind, waiting for a movement in a mole-hill, and then pouncing swiftly. Little training was probably necessary for we have already seen how it is a dog's nature to hunt moles in this way.

Several other methods have been used in the past in an effort to reduce the mole population — one old mole-catcher even wore wooden clogs with which to flatten the molehills! It is difficult to understand what he achieved by this except to inconvenience the moles which then had to throw the soil up again to clear their tunnels. Certainly this method would neither harm them nor force them to move on elsewhere.

Figure 3.10 **Use of dogs**
A terrier can be trained to hunt moles by travelling silently over the ground inhabited by the moles and pouncing when one surfaces.

Use of Guns

It is possible to shoot moles with a shotgun. Although only a few will be killed in this way, it is a sport which is sometimes pursued by farmers and gardeners. Patience is needed, for the wait by a molehill until the soil is seen to move may be a long one. The moment the mole's snout shows it must be shot for if it senses danger it will disappear from view immediately. However, this method will in no way reduce an infestation of the creatures.

Sometimes mothballs were used as a temporary deterrent. Lumps of acetylene were also placed in the runs. Mostly these methods were the attempts of an irate landowner who later had to resort to employing a mole-catcher.

Certain plants were supposed to repel moles; for example, *Euphorbia lathrys*, the Caper Spurge, sometimes known as "Mole Spurge". As noted earlier, moles do not like ground in which either garlic, leeks or onions are grown and the reader is advised to watch mole movements in his vegetable garden and note how the animals avoid tunnelling close to these particular crops.

Mole Squibs

Mole Squibs, a kind of firework which gives off a thick smoke, are sometimes used against moles. However, they merely move them to another area where the task of killing them has to be undertaken. Yet this device is useful for clearing tennis-courts or football pitches quickly.

Further deterrents

There is an old belief that a mole whose nose is pricked by a thorn dies. Surely this is a myth, for during the course of its burrowing life a mole must cut its snout several times. Yet briars were frequently used for this purpose on the continent in years gone by, although it is debatable whether or not any degree of success was obtained. Gardeners who are desperate to repel moles from their lawns or herbacious borders sometimes dig a deep trench around the perimeter and fill it with broken glass.

57

Panda Stancliad

Figure 3.11 **Shooting**

Sometimes farmers destroy moles by blasting the moving soil of a molehill with a shotgun. There are, however, obvious disadvantages to this method due to the time factor involved.

Small-mesh netting would probably have the same effect but it must be buried to a depth of at least 3 feet, for moles will not be deterred easily.

THE TRAPPING SEASON

So every year the army of mole-catchers appeared on the rural scene towards the end of October. Mostly they were 'loners', each jealous of his own particular skill; a few living in horse-drawn caravans, Romany style, others finding shelter in farm outbuildings. They had their own individual areas to trap, coming back year after year, and often a newcomer to the trade had difficulty in finding a territory to work.

With the advent of November trapping was in full swing, the catcher spending his days inspecting his traps and re-siting those which did not catch. In the evenings he skinned the moles which

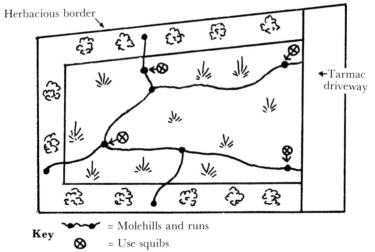

Herbacious border

←Tarmac driveway

Key   ∿∿●∿∿ = Molehills and runs

⊗ = Use squibs

Figure 3.12   **Mole Squibs**

Here, moles are using the lawn as a thoroughfare from the drive to the herbacious borders. Squibs should be used at the entrance and exit points but are only effective over a small area. The idea is to clear the lawn of mole activity rather than to destroy them completely.

59

he had caught during the day, stretching the pelts on wooden boards and leaving them to dry; sometimes dealing with thirty or forty per day. Fresh moles always came in handy for 'scenting' new traps.

Frank Weale was an advocate of the Duffus Trap, preferring this more expensive instrument to the common 'scissors' type. One third of the money earned from the sale of his pelts was invested in new traps until he had built up a full armoury.

PELTS

Sometimes we come across old pictures of lines of dead moles hung on fences and we wonder why the old mole-catchers did not skin these and sell the pelts. There were, in fact, a variety of reasons. In some cases an experienced and well-known catcher in a particular locality was well paid for his services and did not need the extra income nor the additional labour. The corpses were his hallmark, as they were to the gamekeeper who proved his skill to his employer by the head of vermin displayed on the gibbet.

The quality of the pelts also determined whether or not they were worth skinning. During the winter months, when the fur was of a high quality, they maintained their price, but with the coming of spring, after the December moult when the pelts were poorer, the trapper did not consider skinning worthwhile. Therefore, he hung his moles on a fence in full view of passers-by, hoping that his efforts would be noticed by a neighbouring landowner who would then consider him as a trapper for the following season, in preference to his present employee.

THE END OF AN ERA

The outbreak of World War II heralded the end of an era of mole-catching. The countryside was changing, with a growing population demanding a better standard of living. Fashions

Figure 3.13 The end of an era — with extensive areas of farmland, shown above, to rid of moles the farmer soon turned from the old mole-catcher and his traps to the man from the Ministry and his poisons.

were changing, too, for no longer were moleskins in demand and landowners soon discovered that the man from the ministry provided an easier way of ridding the fields of an infestation of moles.

No longer did the mole-catchers appear when the leaves on the trees began to turn brown; yet the art of mole-catching was not gone forever. A few of the older generation, reluctant to surrender the only way of life they knew, continued to ply their trade and in some areas their sons and grandsons still carry on; not for them strychnine and gas. The old traps are still as effective as ever. It is from their example that we must learn; an art rather than purely a means of eradicating moles from an area. It is all part of our heritage as well as a worthwhile hobby.

4

Mole-Catching
Today

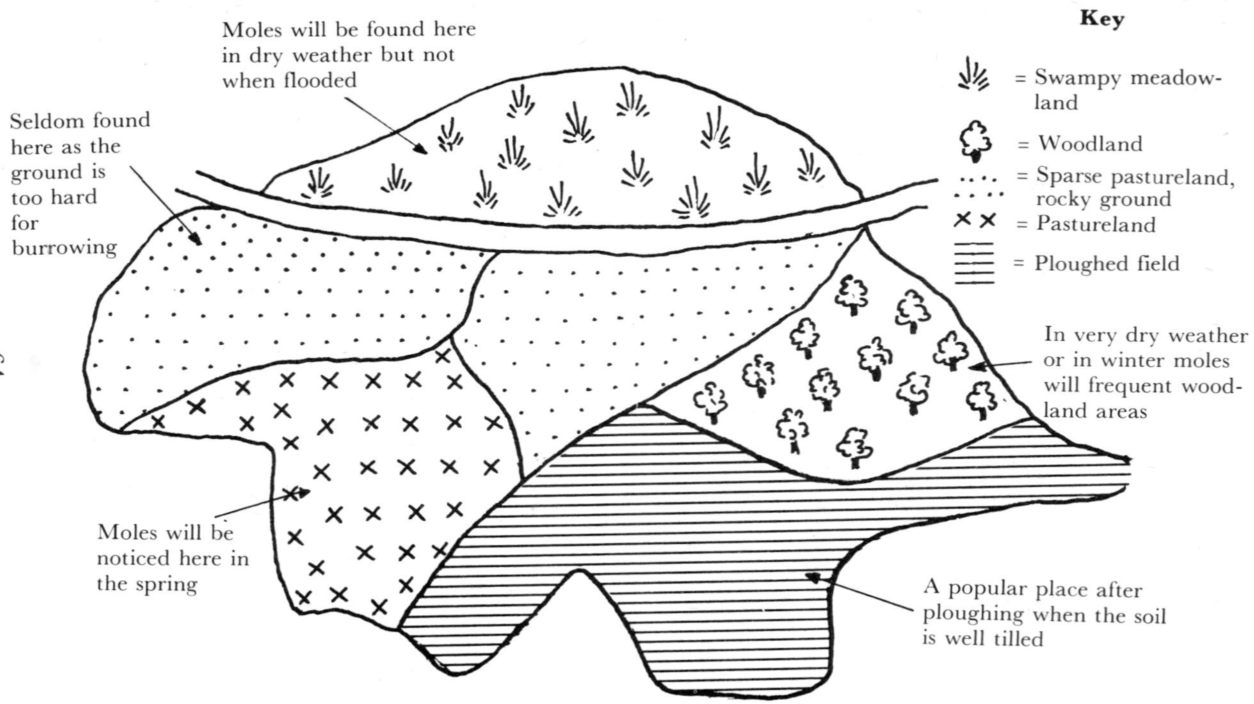

Key

⚘ = Swampy meadow-land

🌳 = Woodland

⋮ = Sparse pastureland, rocky ground

× × = Pastureland

|||| = Ploughed field

In very dry weather or in winter moles will frequent wood-land areas

A popular place after ploughing when the soil is well tilled

Moles will be found here in dry weather but not when flooded

Seldom found here as the ground is too hard for burrowing

Moles will be noticed here in the spring

64

Figure 4.1 **When and where to find moles**

MOLE-CATCHING TODAY

METHODS OF CONTROL

As noted earlier in the preceding chapter, moles may be moved on by using squibs or other methods or, alternatively, they may be exterminated by the use of traps or poisons.

In this chapter the main methods are examined:
1. Traps
2. Gassing
3. Poisons

These are followed by a summary of research carried out by the Ministry of Agriculture which allows the reader to see what results may be obtained. Although mole trapping is not difficult, do not expect anything near 100% success. Moles are cunning creatures and although very vulnerable when above ground, they have learnt to survive in their natural habitat underground.

The main rules of trapping, expanded later where appropriate, are as follows:
1. Observe the mole hills at regular intervals to detect where moles are active.
2. Set traps in the tunnels or burrows. The best results may be obtained from setting in newly made burrows in the evening, preferably just before rain.
3. Examine the traps each day and where appropriate reset them.
4. When using a spade to dig a space for traps, work quietly and carefully, thus keeping the disturbance to a minimum.

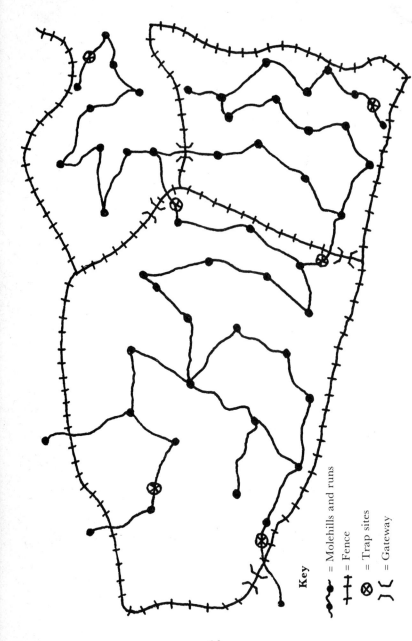

Key

⌇⌇ = Molehills and runs

╫╫ = Fence

⊗ = Trap sites

)(= Gateway

Figure 4.2 **Siting of mole-traps**
The diagram shows a prolific area of mole activity over three fields, but in all probability only a few moles are working here. Too many traps will be a waste of time and effort.

66

As with all other types of trapping, common-sense is the predominating factor. It is no good setting traps in places which are not used by the quarry, so firstly the reader must learn to recognise runs that are in use. Examine the molehills in a field; if they are hard, caked soil with weeds sprouting out of them, then moles are not using the area regularly.

The mole-trapping season lasts, approximately, from November to March, but it is during the first ten weeks that the pelts will fetch the best prices. After the December moult it is barely worth the trouble of skinning your catches.

Traps
The Fenn Mole Trap
To Set: Press **A** down to **B.** Engage end of wire **C** with loop **D.** Open the mole run with a trowel or spade to allow the loops to be firmly embedded in the floor of the run so that the mole has to pass through the loops. The run should be cleaned out and smoothed as much as possible before placing the trap. After setting, exclude any light by covering lightly with herbage and soil. (See Figure 4.3)

When setting traps the following points should be taken into account:

1. Traps work best in straight or travelling runs, rather than amongst the mounds of soil.
2. The best runs may be found round the outside of a field.
3. Good places may be found where runs cross gateways and paths.

These traps are not visible to unauthorised eyes when set, being below ground level, which also helps to protect them from damage by farm vehicles.

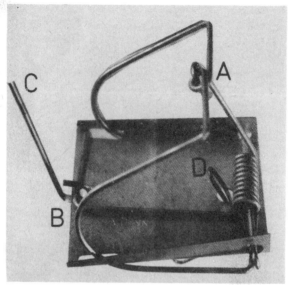

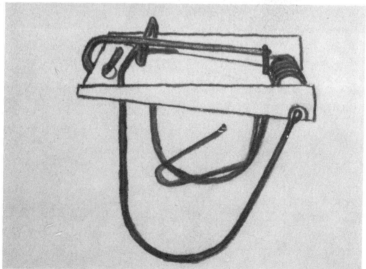

Figure 4.3 **Fenn 'Loop-type' mole-trap** — this trap may be set by following the directions on page 67. (*Courtesy:* A.A. Fenn)

The Duffus Trap

Apart from the new Fenn Mole Trap, the Duffus is the most recent trap in general use today. Legend has it that this light and extremely effective trap was invented in Perthshire early this century. A "one-man Duffus factory" was reported to be in business in the Carse O'Gowrie in recent years.

However, the principle of the Duffus Mole Trap was incorporated in a mouse-trap used in the middle of the last century. Before poison became widely used, the Duffus trap was rapidly becoming the favourite trap of the professional mole-catcher. Its one drawback is that it is easily lost and, therefore, the trapper must ensure that every site is clearly marked with a twig.

FINDING MOLE RUNS

Locating mole runs below ground is usually quite simple, although on rocky terrain it does sometimes present problems. Where possible the mole will travel in a direct line and the trapper should, therefore, dig down approximately half way between two molehills. A square should then be cut out to the depth of the spade, as though the intention was to cut either turf or peat, and the soil lifted out as neatly as possible. If this is done cleanly it should be possible to see the tunnel at opposite ends of the hole. Some soil should then be replaced for the bedding of the trap. This should be pressed well down, so that the trap is set directly in line with the route which the mole will take; if set too low or too high it will only serve to warn the creature of the interference of Man in its underground domain.

When the trap is set, *carefully* replace the square of soil, taking care neither to obstruct the working of the trap nor to allow daylight to filter down into the tunnel. Fill up any gaps with loose soil, but to facilitate inspection of traps it is best if the square of earth over the trap can be lifted in and out with a minimum of trouble. Fresh digging will only serve to warn the quarry whose senses are very acute.

69

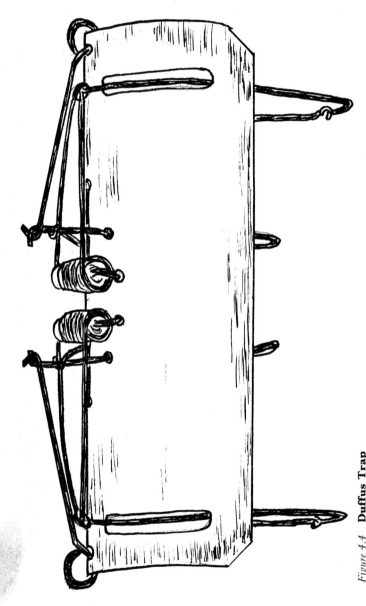

Figure 4.4 **Duffus Trap**
The most recent development in trapping in general use today..

Finding runs, however, is not always as straightforward as there may well be a strata of rock, even one large chunk of stone, beneath the surface which will cause the mole to make a detour between hills. In this case the trapper will not be able to locate the run quite so easily; it will be a matter of trial and error. Once it has been established that there is a rock obstruction, the trapper should test to the right and left of the hard ground to discover its extent. Where it peters out, start to dig down, then take out a square of earth and the run may be found. Failing this, the same method should be tried on the opposite side.

If, however, the mole has gone deep to travel beneath the rock, then it may be necessary to set the trap close to the molehill *but not directly beneath it.*

As mentioned elsewhere in this book, all trapping sites should

Figure 4.5 **Spade** — used by the mole-catcher to dig into the run. (*Photo courtesy:* D. Parfitt)

be clearly marked with a stick otherwise you will surely lose your traps and waste a lot of time needlessly.

TRAPPING

Removing Scent from Traps

All new traps should be buried for a few days prior to use so that any human scent is removed. If traps are required quickly, then they can be boiled to achieve the same result. Unless this is done, it might be several days before your traps stand any chance of catching.

One mole is usually the sole occupant of a hunting area, so by using a freshly killed one to scent your traps you should enjoy increased success. The resident mole will become enraged at the prospect of a rival in his territory and will be that much less cautious as he blunders into the trap.

Setting a trap

Having ascertained that moles are using particular runs, the trapper should now know exactly where and how to set his traps. It is no good setting them directly beneath the mole-hills themselves; they must be set in the runs *linking* the mounds.

Dig down using a sharp spade, removing the soil as carefully as possible until the run is exposed. Place your trap carefully so that it will form part of the tunnel and then replace the soil. If the bottom of the run has been disturbed it should be flattened again, leaving nothing that will make the mole suspicious. Where the soil is light and crumbling, however, only remove sufficient for the trap to be pushed into place, clearing the hole on either side so that the mole's progress is not hindered, otherwise it will burrow beneath the trap. A ploy used by Frank Weale was to place a piece of slate underneath the trap to prevent this happening.

Where traps are set directly beneath molehills, the moles will be pushing the soil in front of them and will spring the traps. A

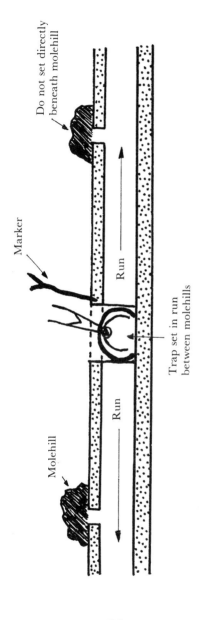

Marker

Molehill

Run

Run

Do not set directly
beneath molehill

Trap set in run
between molehills

Figure 4.6 **Setting a mole trap**
Dig down and place the trap in the run between molehills. It is best if a square of turf is taken out as
it is easily replaced above the trap. Take care not to obstruct the workings of the trap and check
that no daylight is visible from within the run. Mark the sight with a stick to facilitate inspection.

run 15 or 20 yards away will stand a better chance of success. Always replace the soil carefully so that no light shows in the run below. Although the mole's eyesight is poor he can certainly distinguish a shaft of daylight in his usual stygian blackness.

During the course of your trapping you will undoubtedly catch other species such as voles, weasels and mice by accident. However, as all these creatures are harmful in their own ways, a useful job is being done.

Lost traps
Mole traps are easy to lose. They are buried in the ground, often in a sizeable field, and when you come to inspect them your most difficult task is finding them! Valuable time can be lost in this way, and to prevent this it is advised that every trap site is marked by pushing a stick into the ground close to where each trap is set. However, care must be taken that the stick is not pushed down into the mole run beneath.

Sometimes foxes will take both a dead mole and the trap which has caught it. If you discover that one or two of your traps are missing this is probably what has happened.

GASSING

It is not proposed to go into detail concerning the gassing of moles because this method is both dangerous and ineffective. Unlike a rabbit warren, where a number of coneys can be killed at a time in a relatively confined space, moles are solitary creatures, working an extensive area, and it would take large quantities of carbide gas to account for very few of these creatures.

One gardening encyclopaedia advises hydrogen peroxide or calcium cyanide for killing moles. A piece of cotton wool should be soaked with either solution and placed in the run for five minutes, morning and evening. Further advice is given to the effect that the irritation of the human skin produced by this treatment may be soothed by afterwards rubbing in a little lanoline!

POISONING

Poisoning is something to which the amateur should only turn as a last resort. It is simply a means of reducing a mole infestation with the minimum amount of labour. It is unsatisfactory in so much that you never see the results of your labour except that there will be fewer unsightly molehills in the fields.

However, where poisoning is necessary it should be undertaken by the man from the Ministry. Nevertheless, the amateur should be familiar with the method of operation.

Strychnine is the most effective poison for use against moles. **But it must not be used on non-agricultural land without the express permission of the Ministry of Agriculture's divisional executive officer.**

The species of worm to be used is the *Lubricus terrestris* at the ratio of ten to an acre. Avoid using the red-brown brandling worm at any cost. If sufficient worms are available as much as 10lb of strychnine can be used in a day. The worms should be soaked for six hours and, after treating, deposited in couples into the runs, using tweezers and gloves. The soil and turf must be replaced in the same way as when trapping.

Moles die within sixty seconds of taking the poison. Poisoned worms which are not eaten will dissolve after a couple of days. **There is no danger of secondary poisoning to other creatures.** Poisoned moles never go above ground and as they are cannibals they sometimes spread the poison amongst themselves.

Effective as poisoning undoubtedly is in the control of moles, an area which has been cleared soon becomes repopulated as other moles move in. Moles will only really decrease in numbers when their habitat is destroyed, as in the case of flooding.

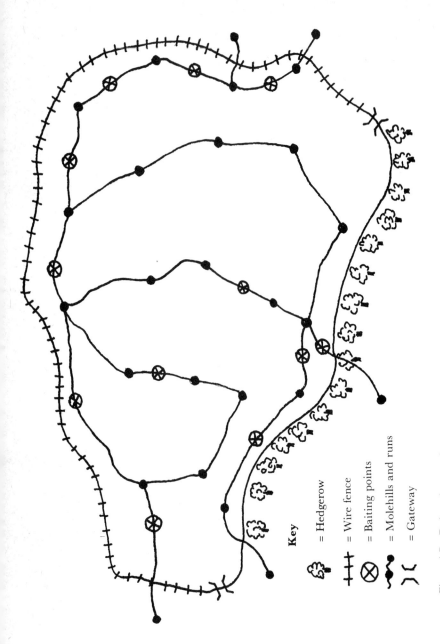

Key

🌿	= Hedgerow
┼	= Wire fence
⊗	= Baiting points
●	= Molehills and runs
)(	= Gateway

Figure 4.7 **Poisoning moles**
Baiting is most successful along fences and hedgerows and in the deeper runs leading to feeding

Recommended method of mole control using strychnine on bait worms

 1. Control is most effective when carried out between October and April.

Proportion of strychnine to worms

 2. 4g of strychnine mixed with a 1lb (453.6g) jar of worms (i.e. one part poison to fifty parts worms).

Preparation of bait

 3. Obtain a quantity of earth worms (not the reddish worm found in manure heaps).

 4. Place the worms in a bucket or similar container containing a piece of wet sacking. The worms will work through the sacking and clean off the soil.

 5. When clean, place the worms in a tin or jar.

 6. Shake the poison over the worms and stir thoroughly with a twig until the poison is evenly distributed over the worms, so that each bait will carry enough poison.

 7. Baits must be fresh and should be used within six hours.

Placing of baits

 8. Bait the deeper main runs leading to the feeding areas; these are often near wire fences or hedgerows. Baiting should be carried out where moles are active.

 9. Using a dibber, make a hole in the mole run. Place one of the poisoned worms in the run with a forked stick or long forceps. Cover the hole with a piece of soil or grass to exclude light.

 10. A minimum of ten baits per acre will be required for a heavily and fairly evenly infested area. It may be necessary to re-treat areas of heavy infestation.

Safety precautions

 11. Avoid touching the poison with bare hands or allowing it to come into contact with clothing. Do not smoke when handling strychnine or prepared baits.

 12. Protect any cuts or abrasions by wearing rubber gloves when handling the poison.

13. When mixing bait, do so in a place where the poison will not blow about.
14. The container holding the poisoned worms should be held as close as possible to the hole during the baiting operation, to reduce the possibility of poisoned worms being dropped accidentally and remaining on the surface of the ground.
15. Unused bait should be deeply buried. Containers and all other equipment including twigs must be well cleaned, or if no longer required, buried.
16. After use, or before eating, drinking or smoking, thoroughly wash hands and gloves.
17. Proper precautions must be taken to prevent access to the poison by other animals.

NOTE: Under the Poisons Rules the strychnine obtained on a permit may be used for no other purposes than the destruction of moles. It will be an offence against the *Protection of Animals Acts* **1911 to 1927 to omit to take all reasonable precautions to prevent injury to dogs, cats, fowls or other domestic animals and wild birds.**

Other methods of controlling moles are mentioned in **Advisory Leaflet 318** issued by the Ministry of Agriculture, Fisheries and Food. Further advice on dealing with them is obtainable from the Ministry's divisional offices.

SKINNING

Any creature which has to be controlled, and which has a saleable pelt, should be skinned. Failure to do this is nothing short of waste, and although single moleskins do not command high prices, in considerable numbers your efforts can be well worthwhile. The pelts are generally used in the making of waistcoats and breeches, and occasionally caps.

It is important that the mole is skinned properly otherwise its market value is at once devalued. There is nothing difficult in the task, and the more you skin the better you will become at it. No two mole-catchers skin their catches in exactly the same way, but the following guide is intended for beginners, and if from this they develop their own technique then so much the better.

Points to follow

1. Moles should be skinned as soon as possible after being killed. The pelt will peel off that much more easily and is less inclined to tear.
2. Using a razor-blade slit the skin on the underside right up to the jaw.
3. Slit the underside of all four legs right up to the feet.
4. Working from the rear, pull the hindlegs out first, peel the skin down to the front legs, then pull them out before attempting the head. You may spoil your first few but persevere until you have mastered the knack. Wash off blood and flesh with soapy water.
5. Tack the skin out on a wooden board, stretching it to at least 4 x 5 inches, and leave it to dry. **Do not treat it with any preservative.** The furrier prefers to do this himself.

It is also wise to ensure that mice cannot get at the skins for they will attempt to nibble them in search of any remaining strips of fat and will ruin them. Skins should be dried in a shed where there is a constant current of air. Damp places such as cellars will cause them to go mouldy.

Pelts are generally ready for sending to the furrier in about a fortnight. However, some advice on packing may not come amiss as, having completed the process successfully so far, all your time and labour will have been wasted if they are damaged or go astray in the post.

Figure 4.8 **Skinning a mole**
1. Slit underside from beneath the jaw to the tail.
2. Peel skin from backlegs.
3. Pull from rear until front legs are reached.
4. Peel skin from front legs.
5. Tack pelt onto boards, stretching as much as possible. The best size for a stretched skin is 4 x 5 inches.

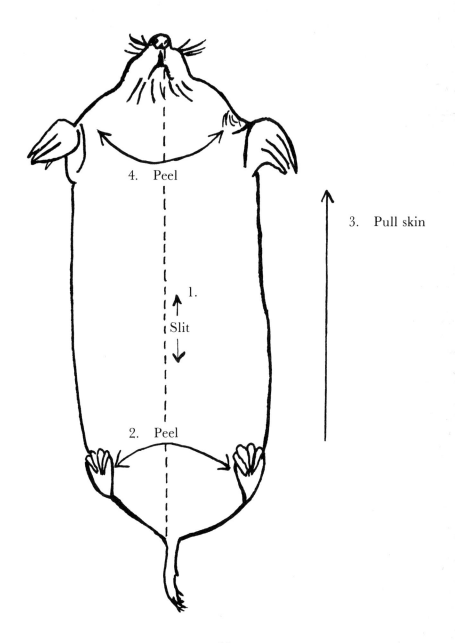

3. Pull skin

4. Peel

1.
Slit

2. Peel

81

Packing skins for posting
1. Roll individual skins in a layer of newspaper.
2. Use an inner layer of either sheets of newspaper or corrugated paper.
3. The outer wrapping should be of thick brown paper.
4. Address the parcel clearly and also write your own name and address on the outside. Mark it "perishable goods – with care!"
5. **Pay a compensation fee when you post your parcel.** This will ensure that if the package goes astray you will not be out of pocket.
6. Allow at least a fortnight in which to receive a reply from the furrier. He will have many parcels daily containing skins of different species and usually deals with them in rotation.

A reputable furrier will make you the best offer he can. Where these fall below your own estimated figure it is generally due to one of two causes:
1. Pelts which have been torn in skinning, even if only slightly.
2. Poor quality furs which may be due either to local factors or because moles have been killed after the December moult.

No animal in our countryside today should be hunted solely for financial gain. Yet when it is necessary to control a creature in the interests of farming, forestry or conservation then every effort should be made to avoid wastage by the sale of skins or feathers. There will be no profit if time and labour are taken into consideration. The income from such sales will merely help to offset the initial outlay of traps and other equipment.

82

CLOTHING

In olden times the mole-catcher was generally recognisable by his "uniform" of moleskins. Today, however, this attire would be considered more of a luxury. When mole-catching you need to wear light but warm clothing. Most of the time you will be on the move, stopping every so often to dig and set a trap. Seldom will you be standing for long periods like the wildfowler or the gamekeeper, but you will be in exposed places, pastureland that has little to offer in the way of shelter. Waterproof clothing is essential if you are to be comfortable throughout the day. You must also wear garments which allow freedom of movement.

A COMPARISON OF TRAP EFFICIENCY

The following is reproduced by kind permission of the Ministry of Agriculutre, Fisheries and Food.

"The **'Pincer'**, the **'Dufus'** and the wooden **'Whole-barrel'** trap were laid by two operators and a record kept of the number of days each trap was set, the captures made, the occasions when it was sprung without capture and also when it was avoided by the mole. Each of the traps used was identified by a numbered brass disc. At the site of each trap setting the type used was randomly selected by the drawing of lots.

The traps were set for two days each week for thirteen weeks and sixty moles were caught. The results are given in Table I and the efficiency of each trap may be compared by reference to Table 2. It will be seen that all three types of trap had equal opportunities for catching moles (Group 1). The other results (Groups 2, 3 and 4), show the 'Pincer' trap to have the highest percentage of captures both in relation to traps set and to traps sprung. This trap also had the fewest instances of avoidance. Although the 'Duffus' trap showed a lower percentage of captures than the 'Pincer' trap it was also reasonably effective. The 'Duffus' trap is the only trap designed to catch two moles at one setting. There were two occasions when a double capture was made, one in mid-December and the other in late January; in both instances the two animals were of opposite sex. Its main drawback was that it was more frequently avoided (43 times) than the 'Pincer' (22 times) in approximately the same number of settings.

The wooden 'Whole-barrel' trap was found unsuitable in this study and was very inefficient in every respect when compared with the other traps.

Unlike the 'Pincer' trap the 'Duffus' trap caught six moles by some part of one or both fore-limbs. Two of these moles were alive on examination. In three instances where the trap had been sprung with no capture, there was hair and smooth compact soil on the trap which indicated that a trapped mole had escaped. These faulty captures could be accounted for, in some instances, by the wire noose becoming misaligned so that it was positioned too close to the trigger. The evidence suggests that this would allow the trap to be sprung, presumably by an outstretched fore-limb, before the vulnerable parts of the mole had passed through

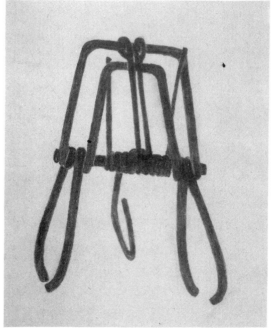

Figure 4.9 **Fenn 'Pincer-type' mole-trap**
(*Courtesy:* A.A. Fen)

84

the noose. In every case where the 'Pincer' and 'Duffus' trap caught moles in the region of the thorax or abdomen the animal was dead when the traps were inspected.

At the Grassland Research Institute the soil varied from sandy loam, sandy clay and loam over chalk to mainly chalk. Although in this study the type of soil did not appear to influence the success of either the 'Duffus' or the 'Pincer' trap, moist soil was found better than dry crumbly soil. When the soil was very wet, but not waterlogged, following the thawing of deep snow, the percentage of captures in relation to traps sprung (captures and misses) and avoided was 45% compared with 35% for the whole experiment.

Moles often avoid traps; evidence of this is shown when traps are found filled with earth, sprung with no capture, bypassed by a new run, pushed out of the ground or when the runs are blocked. This avoidance may be associated with imperfect trapping techniques and sometimes with faults in the structure of the trap, coupled with the very sensitive reaction of the mole to changes in its tunnel system. The excavation of the site in which to lay a trap results in damage to the run which must be repaired. Loose earth and foreign matter left in the run, or a misaligned trap will disturb the continuity of the run and will increase the chance of avoidance.

Faults in traps are not always obvious. A 'Pincer' trap had a record of eight misses and no captures, on careful examination it was found to have a maximum aperture, when set, of 3.3 cm which was smaller than any other examples of this trap. The gripping arms were of a slightly different shape from the others and this constricted still further the entrance to the trap.

Trap	Days set	Captures	Misses		Untouched
			Sprung	Avoided	
Pincer	314	32	8	22	252
Duffus	320	26*	6	43	247
Whole-barrel	134	2	1	31	100
Total all traps	768	60	15	96	599

Table 1 - Results of trapping moles with three types of trap

* Includes two instances of a double capture on the same trap day.

85

Group		Traps		
		Pincer	Duffus	Whole-barrel
1.	Percentage of traps sprung (captures and misses) and avoided in relation to settings*	20	23	25
2.	Percentage captured in relation to settings*	10	8	1.5
3.	Percentage captured in relation to traps sprung (captures and misses) and avoided	52	35	6
4.	Percentage of trap misses (sprung and avoided) in relation to settings*	10	15	24

Table 2 – Comparison of the efficiency of three types of mole trap

* Settings = number of traps x number of days set.

The Efficiency of Control by Trapping

"In order to test the efficiency of trapping as a method of control over a long period, an employee of the Grassland Research Institute, who had no previous experience of either the 'Pincer' or the 'Duffus' trap, was instructed in the use of traps. He was supplied with eighteen traps of each type and was free to use whichever suited the trapping site. He found that the 'Pincer' trap was generally more suitable and more successful than the 'Duffus' trap.

"A summary of the results of the two years' trapping period is given in Table 3. The reduction in numbers caught in the second year compared with the first year corresponds with a decrease in the amount of mole activity.

Trapping period	Method of capture				Total
	Pincer	Duffus	Wooden whole-barrel	By hand	
First year	76	47	2	1	126
Second year	38	4	—	2	44
Total for two years	114	51	2	3	170

Table 3 - Results of two years' trapping

"In the two-year period 170 moles were caught. The number caught in each month was:

Month	Jan	Feb	Mar	Apr	May	June	July	Aug	Sept	Oct	Nov	Dec	Total
No. of]moles	27	54	32	6	3	1	0	0	6	9	4	28	170

Table 4 - Total number of moles caught

The marked seasonal variation in trapping returns is to be expected as it reflects the increased trapping in winter, when mole damage and mole workings are easily seen, and decreased trapping in the summer when damage and workings are often hidden by ground cover.

"A survey of the 628 acres of the Institute's grounds was made each November of 1959, 1960 and 1961 when mole activity was recorded and plotted on a 25-inch-to-the-mile map. Immediately prior to the commencment of trapping in 1959, mole activity extended over an area of 81 acres, but by the end of the first year's trapping this had been reduced to 28 acres and at the end of the second year it was 12 acres. Most of the moles remaining at the end of the investigations were in land bordering untrapped property not belonging to the Institute. If these few survivors had been responsible for serious damage they could have been largely

87

trapped out by two or three weeks of sustained trapping effort. A significant immigration of moles from neighbouring land occurred each year and for this reason even complete clearance is unlikely to be permanent. It is concluded that a resident trapper, although mainly engaged on other work, could substantially reduce an extensive mole population and, by trapping fresh immigrants when first noticed, could prevent serious reinfestation in the future."

I would like to thank Messrs. C. Meen and R. Minchin for their assistance with the trapping and to the Director and Staff of the Grassland Research Institute, Berkshire for their help and cooperation.

5
A Professional
Mole Catcher

Figure 5.1 **Veteran mole-catcher** — here we see him lifting a Barrel Trap.
(*Courtesy*: David Imrie)

A PROFESSIONAL MOLE-CATCHER

Frank Weale was established as a professional mole-catcher by the time he was twenty-five years of age. This particular corner of south-west Shropshire did not benefit from the autumnal infiltration of the 'catchers, as did other parts of the country, and as a result work was plentiful. His skill was undoubted, and he had a volume of work to contend with, being in great demand in this upland sheep country where whole hillsides were covered with molehills.

METHOD AND SYSTEM

On a typical day Weale would set forth soon after daylight, carrying a bag of traps on his back. An experienced man such as this could cover much more ground than a novice, a cursory glance being enough to tell him whether or not moles were working a particular area. He used a ratting spade, similar to the one illustrated and described in the author's book *Ratting and Rabbiting for Amateur Gamekeepers* and could set a trap inside thirty seconds.

Frank Weale was a systematic worker, preferring a network of adjoining farms to odd ones scattered here and there. On his first day in "new territory" he would trap two farms and then on the following day he removed his traps from Farm A and concentrated on the runs on Farm C. In the afternoon he returned to Farm B and took up the traps which he had set there in readiness for setting them on Farm D at daybreak the next day. In this way he killed scores of moles, like a one-man army conquering a country which it had invaded, ploughing relentlessly through the ranks of the enemy. Most of the old 'catchers worked a farm here and another a mile or two further on. Weale claimed that his "system" made great inroads into the country's mole population.

Certainly Frank Weale made a better living from catching moles than he would have done had he followed his father's labouring on the land. He supported a wife and three children and ran a smallholding as well.

The Mole-catcher in summer

Like the question which children often ask "where do the flies go in winter?", the reader is bound to ask where the mole-catcher goes in summer. Of course, the amateur may, and often does, continue trapping all round the year. Indeed, some of the old professionals used to do so, but only in cases where the payment from the landowner was sufficient for them to manage without the sale of the skins. It is certainly in the interests of the occupier of land, or the game preserver, to kill every mole which he can, for agriculture and game will benefit from it.

Frank Weale put his traps away at the beginning of April. Certainly the farmers would have been willing to pay him for his services throughout the summer, but he preferred to work on his 5 acres of land. For the amateur, mole-catching is an exciting sport; for the professional it is hard work involving the necessity to walk several miles every day. Once winter was over the 'catchers welcomed a few months of rest and other less arduous tasks.

DAVID IMRIE

Some years ago I struck up a friendship with a professional rabbiter/molecatcher in the Lake District. David Imrie was a regular weekly contributor to the *Shooting Times* for over a quarter of a century and few know more about the countryside than this man.

For many years David lived a solitary existence in a wooden hut in the forest, and although a few years ago he moved down to live in the village, it is the former setting which made a lasting impression on me; a way of life to be envied by the genuine countryman, away from the pressures of a mundane urban existence.

The hut in the forest

The late afternoon sun glinted on the summit of Skiddaw as I turned left over the bridge in Little Braithwaite, and took the narrow road leading upwards into the mountains of the Lake District. The leaves on the trees were beginning to turn a rich golden brown, for it was already mid-October, and there was a nip in the air to remind the visitor to this part of the country that summer had had its fling. It had been fine for a week now, and the sun was still capable of shining for another week but on the other hand the first fall of snow could just as easily cover the hillsides by daybreak. This is one of the uncertanties of life which these hardy Lakeland people learn to live with and accept.

The steepness of the road forced me to change down into bottom gear and then, less than a mile from the village which I had left behind me, I saw the gateway which I was looking for. It stood at the foot of a larch covered hillside, the rough muddy track beyond disappearing into the forest. I had to put the Austin Gypsy into four-wheel drive in order to negotiate this type of terrain, the wheels sinking 3 or 4 inches into the soft surface, as I continued on my way.

I had not far to go, possibly a couple of hundred yards, before I saw my destination. The hut stood there in a large clearing; the last rays of the setting sun filtering through the tall trees and displaying this humble dwelling place in an aura of perfect beauty and peace. There was nothing very remarkable about the shack itself. It was constructed entirely of wood, with a gas-tarred felt roof and a single chimney stack from which a wisp of blue woodsmoke drifted lazily. The large window beside the doorway faced the path up which I had just driven so I was not suprised when the dark green door opened to reveal a man standing on the threshold.

His thick tweed suit of plus-fours was immaculate and his peaked cap, made from the same material, was delightfully pleasing to the eye – when held in contrast to the variety of tattered head gear which many gamekeepers habitually wear. He had one of the kindest faces which I have ever seen and, indeed, this only serves to portray the character of the man. His weatherbeaten complexion was proof enough of a lifetime spent out of doors, and his strong Scottish accent tells one that he has not always lived south of the border.

David is a Scot by birth, although he had spent the last thirty-five years of this life in this hut in the woods above Little Braithwaite. He was a gamekeeper once, in the days when pheasants were hand-reared in their thousands in these vast Lakeland woods, but it is now many years since he has built up, and looked after, a stock of game. No shooting takes place on this estate now and my friend is the only reminder that game-preservation had ever existed there. He first came to live in the hut in the days before World War II as a full-time gamekeeper. It was only to be a temporary residence, until more permanent accommodation could be found for him, but somehow David just stayed on there in that woodland glade. He liked it and was in no hurry to move elsewhere.

The inside of the hut was an education in itself and there is no doubt that the total stranger, on entering, would be completely amazed at its contents. Naturally, there were the usual tools and appliances of the countryman to be found there – several boxes of cartridges were stacked on the mantleshelf, whilst a couple of shotguns resided in the far corner beside a heap of rabbit snares, a spade and balls of thick twine. It was the remainder of the room which was so out of character with this impedimenta. The walls opposite the door, and the one behind the fireplace, were lined with shelves on which almost every type of book imaginable was to be found. If one notices the typewriter, and

Figure 5.2 **David Imrie** — gamekeeper and mole-catcher extraordinaire.

possibly the neatly type-written sheets of paper in the far corner of the room, then the reason for this profusion of books is not so hard to discover, for David has been a writer for many years now. His articles have appeared regularly in many of our sporting journals since about 1935, and he has had two full-length books on gamekeeping published. His knowledge of the ways of the countryside is unlimited but, most important of all, he has the gift of being able to transcribe this on to paper, something which is rare amongst men whose very living is earned in the fields and coverts.

However, David is a gamekeeper no longer, due to the neglect of the sporting side of this Lakeland estate, but is employed part-time in methods of rabbit and mole control. He is responsible for several thousand acres of land and must see to it that the once prolific coney does not breed in any large numbers. He is on call to every tenant farmer within these boundaries and, more often than not, a call for help is answered the following day. His bicycle is his only means of transport and it is a familiar sight to see him riding through the narrow lanes with his gun slung on his shoulder, and a tin of rabbit gas and a gross of snares tied behind his saddle.

Many times, during a cold spell in winter, did I spare a thought for my friend. I pictured him huddling over his small fire, seeking every vestige of warmth possible, whilst a blizzard relentlessly raged in the forest outside. He admits that his home was sometimes very cold during the winter months, but this was preferable to the excessive heat of summer. The thin walls allow the outside temperature to dominate within and about this he can do little but, by stoking the fire up to its capacity, it is possible to combat the freezing conditions. All that he can do to overcome a heat-wave is to sleep with the door wide open all night, in an attempt to alleviate the stifling atmosphere within. He may be deprived of many of the luxuries which we take for granted but, overall, he is attaining a much greater knowledge and understanding of the world about us than we are ourselves.

Deer often grazed within a few yards of his hut, and the

Figure 5.3 **Fallow Deer** — often these timid creatures would be found grazing within a few yards of David Imrie's hut.

patient observer at the window, overlooking the glade, always saw something of profound interest. Pheasants, hares, grey squirrels, jays, magpies, kestrels, buzzards and a host of others are all to be seen from this clearing in the wooded hillside, and for the true countryman there is never a dull moment.

Most men would have found difficulty in keeping their sanity if they had lived for thirty-five years in such solitary places as my good friend. Possibly one man in a thousand is suited to such a life, but few could stand it for such long periods. Lighthouse-keepers usually do no more than a stretch of three months work without a lengthy break, and even then they are subjected to severe medical and physcological tests. David, however, would not change with any man. I asked him once if he had ever considered leaving the hut, and moving nearer to civilization. He confessed that he had only once debated with himself over this, during a period when he was confined to bed with a severe dose of influenza. It is a terrible thought to be lying very ill in bed, with not another soul knowing of one's condition, and fearing lest pneumonia might set in. He gave considerable thought to the wisdom of this hermit-like existence during this time of illness, but once his health returned, and he began to get up and about again, he dismissed any notions of leaving. Only a similar occurrence would give rise to such thoughts of leading a more conventional life.

His visitors at the hut were frequent, such as myself, calling on him at intervals throughout the year, but mostly these were in the summer months and it was only during the dead of winter that he was really alone. Then he turned to his bagpipes, and his typewriter, for companionship.

Why did my friend David choose to live in the manner in which has for all those years? Only he knows the answer to this question, and when asked he will simply reply that he preferred this type of existence to any other. In all fairness, it certainly has its compensations as well as its drawbacks.

David has one or two other duties to perform on the estate beside rabbit control. He is required to carry out extensive foot patrols during weekends in the summer months, keeping a watchful eye open for trespassers and picnickers who light fires to brew their tea and endanger the forestry plantations and tinder dry heather. This is quite an arduous task with such a large area to cover, and he can quite honestly say that his time is fully taken up with this work on Saturdays and Sundays. Occasionally he takes time off to go fell-climbing — a chance to take some useful wildlife photographs.

It is now some time since I last saw David. Periodically I receive letters from him, and these I treasure, for they are mostly accounts of wildlife and his own observations. A lengthy letter, some time ago, set out the arguments for and against the woodcock carrying her young. He writes of a caller who claims to have witnessed this actually taking place, but my friend openly disbelieves him. Nobody has yet provided proof that this bird carries her chick, and this controversial question has been the cause of many heated arguments since before the turn of the century.

He wrote to me once concerning a man who claimed to be able to call foxes effectively, with the mouth alone, and my friend spent a fruitless night out under the full moon with him, in freezing conditions, all to no avail. His letters are a lesson in nature itself, and I have learned more from them than from all the books which I have studied on the subject. The neatly written sheets have an atmosphere all of their own, seeming to echo the call of the wild geese on their way to Derwentwater, the cronking of the ravens, the mewing of the buzzards over Skiddaw, and the challenging cry of the stags at rutting time in the forests above Braithwaite.

I am honoured that David is a close friend of mine. It is a relationship which I shall never let drift away, for to know him is to know life itself. The sound of his bagpipes in an evening is synonomous with the nocturnal calls of the wild in the forest surrounding his shack. The two are inseparable.

I share his sadness at his move from the hut in the forest but this was something which was inevitable as the years passed.

Fortunately, he still has good health and here is one rabbiter and mole-catcher who still carries on in the old tradition, a link with an era which has almost gone, working the warrens and mole-runs on the Lingholm Estate.

David Imrie's advice on mole-catching
David Imrie has destroyed moles on and off since the age of fourteen, but from 1960-1973 he combined gamekeeping with mole control for the **Above Derwent Rabbit Clearance Society Ltd.** which was supervised by the Ministry of Agriculture, Fisheries and Food. In the beginning he used the Duffus Trap which catches independently at either end, but the economic factor forced him to resort to poison — time simply was not available to visit all traps daily. The disadvantage with Duffus Traps is that they have to be lifted wholly out of the ground, a time-consuming factor. However, no cruelty is caused if a Duffus Trap is not inspected every day, and the loss is purely a financial one to the man who is concerned with selling his moleskins. Due to the lightness of this type of trap it is sometimes dug up and taken away, together with its catch, by a fox. David cannot recollect having lost a Scissors or Barrel Trap in this way.

Poison
The secret of successful poisoning is being liberal with the lethal bait, which consists of earthworms treated sparingly with strychnine. As much poison crystals as would lie on a 1 pence coin is sufficient to treat a 1lb jar of washed earthworms. The operator must be extremely careful when using strychnine, as a grain and a half is sufficient to kill a human being. If a comparable poison could be found the Ministry of Agriculture would cease to issue permits for strychnine.

Unlike mole traps, poison bait for the destruction of these creatures should be laid in underground galleries among fresh heaps. For this task the operator must be equipped with a 'proddle' and a pair of long-handled tweezers. He must **never** touch the bait with his hands. On the other hand, the trapper may find the 'killing runs' among the old heaps or even below fence wires where no heaps are visible. These old-established runs can often produce moles for many days.

When David was destroying moles for the Above Derwent Society he had to climb 1,000 feet to some of the Skiddaw Intakes which only serves to illustrate that moles are to be found in high places, providing food is plentiful. The author himself lives at 1,000 feet above sea level and in the fields surrounding his home there are always moles to be found.

CHANGING TIMES

Truly World War II heralded the end of an era of mole-catching. Between 1939-45 little was done to check the mole's population, but with the cessation of hostilities and a return to normal farming, this animal's control was a necessity. Autumn came but the mole-catchers no longer arrived in their numbers. Only a few kept up the old tradition for there was more money to be earned elsewhere.

The agricultural authorities realised just how detrimental the mole was to the farmer and now a new kind of war was about to be declared. The mole had to be destroyed in large numbers with the minimum amount of time and labour. Traps were too slow and too expensive. Strychnine was much more deadly and very much cheaper. Moleskins, too, were going out of fashion. It hardly made the part-time trapper's efforts worthwhile.

Yet the mole-catcher was not destined to disappear entirely from the rural scene. A few still carried on the trade, their sons following them, pursuing a way of life which they were determined should not die. Strangely, they still found an abundance of work. The older generation of farmers were reluctant to succumb to "new-fangled" methods of mole control. They had no faith in the characterless operators with their supplies of strychnine-dosed worms. Far rather would they see a line of dead moles hanging from the top strand of a barbed-

Figure 5.4 **The gibbet**
Dead moles hanging on a fence — proof of the skill of the mole-catcher but also a sure sign that
fetching high prices.

Paul Blincow

wire fence. At least they could see for themselves that the creatures were dead!

Thus the reader himself, upon practising mole-catching in the traditional way, becomes one of the specialists at this particular form of vermin control. Not only will he be carrying out a useful job, but he will be spending many enjoyable hours in Nature's own domain, and also continually learning about all other aspects of the countryside. Mole-catching is an integral part of gamekeeping and conservation.

APPENDIX

Some useful addresses for the mole-catcher.

Poisoning
Where it is necessary to poison moles, advice should first be sought from the Regional Pest Officer, Ministry of Agriculture, Fisheries & Food. Consult a telephone directory to find your local officer.

Traps
Makers and suppliers.

Messrs A, Fenn,
F.H.T. Works,
High Street,
Astwood Bank,
Redditch,
Worcester

} Loop type and Pincer type

Swinnerton & Co. (Stourbridge) Ltd.,
Platts Road,
Amblecote,
Stourbridge,
West Midlands. DY8 4YR
Telephone: Stourbridge 4259 & 5959
After business hours: Stourbridge 5095

} Duffus Trap and Scissors Trap

Buyers of Skins

Siaco Furs and Skins Ltd.,
16, Queenhithem,
Upper Thames Street,
London, EC4V 3HA.
Telephone: 01-236 4520

} Mole skins, also buyers of fox and mink skins

INDEX

107